THE
GREEK DOCTOR'S DIET
COOKBOOK

100 delicious, Mediterranean-inspired, low-GL
recipes to help you stay slim and healthy for life

DR FEDON ALEXANDER LINDBERG

RODALE

Contents

This edition first published in 2006 by
Rodale International Ltd
7–10 Chandos Street
London W1G 9AD
www.rodalebooks.co.uk

Copyright © 2006 Rodale International Ltd
Text © Fedon Alexander Lindberg
Food photography © Jonathan Gregson
Food styling by Angela Boggiano
Location photography in Greece © Mats Widén
Art direction and design by Simon Daley at Giraffe
Editors: Maggie Ramsay and Jillian Stewart
Production: Sara Granger

www.drlindberg.com
www.greekdoctorsdiet.com

A CIP record for this book is available from the British Library
ISBN 13: 978-1-4050-9327-9
ISBN 10: 1-4050-9327-7

Printed and bound by Star Standard Industries (PTE), Singapore, using acid-free
paper from sustainable sources.

1 3 5 7 9 8 6 4 2

This edition distributed to the book trade by Pan Macmillan Ltd

NOTICE
This book is intended as a reference volume only, not as a medical manual.
The information given here is designed to help you make informed decisions about
your health. It is not intended as a substitute for any treatment that you may have
been prescribed by your doctor. If you suspect that you have a medical problem,
we urge you to seek competent medical help.

Front cover photograph: Chicken kebabs with fresh herbs

RODALE
LIVE YOUR WHOLE LIFE™

We inspire and enable people to improve their lives and the world around them

With special thanks to Per Lauritz Lien, our wonderful and creative chef at the clinic in Oslo, who helped me create and test many of the recipes, to the delight of our 'test panel'. I would also like to thank my 'Norwegian mom' Wera, for her unbeatable chocolate cake recipe; Mats Widén for his beautiful photography and wonderful memories of our trip to Greece; my superb editor Maggie Ramsay, and all those who have contributed to this book. It has been a pleasure.

Introduction

It is dark outside; only the stars give out a gentle light this moonless summer night. The air is warm and dry, and the whole family – parents, grandparents and siblings – are sitting outside, around the large dinner table on the veranda of our summer home. The enticing smell of sea bream and octopus cooking on the grill competes with the delicate scent of gardenia and jasmine from the garden. The table is covered with countless little dishes of meze: Greek salad with feta cheese and oregano, lima beans in tomato sauce, calamari, prawns saganaki, lamb meatballs with mint and anise, the obligatory tzatziki, stuffed vine leaves, chickpea croquettes…

This idyllic evening reminds me of when I was growing up in Greece in the late sixties and early seventies. Life was definitely much simpler then. There were no mobile phones, no internet; there may have been fewer choices but there was also less pressure and more time to spend with family and friends. Nowadays we have more material goods than ever, but few of us are content. We may live longer, but that is mostly thanks to expensive medicines and advanced medical technology, not because of a better lifestyle. We live stressful lives struggling to meet all our commitments, we undertake little or no physical activity and much of the food we eat is denatured and highly processed. We manage, nonetheless, to achieve and experience more than previous generations could have imagined. But are we happier or healthier?

Greeks, like many other Mediterranean people, have always been very fond of good food and recognized how important it is as part of a happy, healthy life. As far back as the 4th century BC, some

2,500 years ago, Archestratos, from the Greek colony of Syracuse, was busy writing the world's first cookbook, *Gastronomia*. In it, he described in detail not only a great number of recipes, but also ingredients and where they could be bought. He knew which fish could be found in the markets of Carthago or Pella and where to find the best bakers in Athens. He thought highly of eel from the Kopais lake near Athens (now dried out), wine from the islands of Thassos and Lesbos, and fried sardines from Faliron on the coast of Athens. It is fascinating to read about these ancient food markets and it is clear that there was an abundant and varied supply of foods from the Mediterranean and Black Sea. However, what is just as interesting is that the social aspect of eating and drinking with family and friends was at least as important as the food itself.

It seems the ancient Greeks had a clear understanding of the real meaning of the 'good life', though perhaps this is hardly surprising given that Greece produced Dionysus, the god of wine and feasting, and Hippocrates, the Father of Medicine (and the man who coined the expression 'Let food be thy medicine'). Hippocrates realized that all disease has a physiological and rational explanation and, contrary to what was once believed, was not the work of the gods! This meant that man had a hand in his own destiny – adequate rest, eating healthily, fresh air and cleanliness would help prevent and cure disease. What these two contrasting 'personalities' represent, I believe, offers us an example of the balance that is needed in order to maintain physical and mental health and well-being. The ancient Greek tradition of celebrating Dionysus was an expression of their love for life and the joy of good food and drink enjoyed with good company. The Hippocratic understanding of how food can prevent and cure disease illustrated their appreciation of wellness and a healthy life. If you add to that equation the ancient Greeks' belief in 'everything in moderation' and 'a sound mind in a sound body' you have a well balanced and simple philosophy of life; one that is just as applicable today as it was in ancient times.

Which foods are most beneficial to our health? There's no simple answer to that, but the Mediterranean diet has long been acclaimed as one of the healthiest in the world. Olive oil, garlic, wine, fish, yogurt, cheese, nuts, pulses, whole grains, fruits and lots of vegetables are the main ingredients. There is of course no single 'Mediterranean diet'; it varies from region to region. The traditional diet specifically of the Greek island of Crete was recognized for its health benefits, explaining the long life expectancy and low risk of heart disease and cancer among the island's population. The best scientific evidence for these health benefits was presented at a large international conference back in 1993, sponsored in part by Harvard University. The traditional Cretan diet is relatively high in fats, well above 40 per cent of total energy, compared with the diets of many western countries that succumbed to the low-fat craze of recent decades. However, most of the fat in the Cretan diet comes from natural, minimally processed sources like olive oil and nuts, and is mainly monounsaturated fat. A substantial body of scientific evidence suggests that it would be wise to greatly reduce the amount of sugar and refined starchy foods – such as white bread, pasta,

rice and potatoes – in the typical western diet, and instead eat more healthy fat from plants and fish. Greek cuisine can be a great source of inspiration for moving in that direction. My dietary approach, described in detail in my first book, *The Greek Doctor's Diet*, is based on the traditional Cretan diet, but updated and revised to take account of the latest information on the Glycaemic Index (GI) and Glycaemic Load (GL). (The former is a method of ranking foods according to how quickly they raise the blood sugar, while the latter takes account of the effect of the amount of carbohydrates we actually eat.) The recipes in this book are based on that diet. They are not designed to be used as a means to short-term weight loss, but as part of a new and better way of eating for life.

Creating the book you hold in your hands has been a delightful project for me. Going back to my roots and travelling in Greece in May was, as always, a delightful experience, and rather different from what the majority of tourists experience at the height of the season in mid summer. The temperature is just right, everything is green and in bloom and the incredible scent of flowers is everywhere; plus the locals are laid back and not yet tired of the hordes of tourists who 'invade' their territory during the summer. Some unforgettable days and nights were spent working on this book in Athens, and on Santorini and Cephalonia, and if even just a little of the enjoyment and love of good food and good company that our team enjoyed comes across in these pages then you will begin to understand the simple pleasure I felt enjoying home-cooked food on that veranda under the stars.

Food, health
and weight

The Greek Doctor's Diet is an easy-to-follow dietary system which can significantly affect the way you feel – as well as the way you look. It is not a quick-fix, but a nutritional concept that you can and should follow for the rest of your life. It does not rely on calorie counting or food restrictions, so you will probably not eat less, just differently from the way you are used to. The diet is based on great-tasting natural foods that will increase well-being and vitality and make it easy to stick to the diet.

The food you eat can contribute in a negative or positive way to your health and quality of life, so it is essential to make wise choices with regard to both the type and amount of the various foods you consume. And that is what the Greek Doctor's Diet is all about – making the right food choices in order to restore a more natural balance of the types of carbohydrates, proteins and fats you eat, and to meet the body's needs for important vitamins, minerals and antioxidants. By improving your diet in this way you will achieve more stable blood sugar, greater hormonal balance and better health.

What can I expect?

If you are overweight, the Greek Doctor's Diet will help you to gradually lose weight. How much and how fast depends on how overweight you are, how precisely you follow the principles, how much you exercise, how much stress you experience and, last but not least, your genes. Except for the first week, when part of the weight loss may be due to loss of fluids, you should not expect to lose more than 1–1.5 kg (2–3 lb) of body fat per week, unless you are very overweight. If you lose more than this, it will affect your muscle mass, which is not good, as it is muscle that keeps the metabolism active.

If you often crave sweets or starches, following the principles of this diet will help you regain control of what you eat.

If you are underweight, the Greek Doctor's Diet will help you reach a healthy weight. If your body weight is already normal, you will neither gain nor lose weight, but you will feel much better.

If you have high blood pressure, elevated cholesterol or high triglycerides, a balanced diet will improve your health and help you avoid cardiovascular disorders.

If you have diabetes, you will find this diet gives you much better control of your blood sugar; your cholesterol and triglyceride levels will be lower and your blood pressure will improve.

If you often feel tired and sluggish an hour or so after a meal, you may suffer from 'reactive hypoglycaemia', a symptom of low blood sugar. This can mean that you are insulin sensitive, and that your blood sugar drops a relatively short time after you have eaten highly refined foods such as white bread, processed cereals and sugar. Following the principles of this diet will prevent or greatly reduce such symptoms.

Allergies, inflammatory conditions like arthritis and asthma, chronic fatigue syndrome, fibromyalgia and stress-related disorders often improve as a result of a change in eating habits. The typical modern diet, with its high intake of sugars and starches and low intake of omega-3 essential fatty acids, may contribute greatly to such problems, because it causes unstable blood sugar levels with accompanying hormonal turbulence. The Greek Doctor's Diet can help by stabilizing blood sugar levels and improving hormonal balance.

So this is far more than just a weight-loss diet. Following the principles of this diet will help keep your blood sugar stable throughout the day, keeping you mentally alert and physically fit. The Greek Doctor's Diet is designed to help you do everything you can to prevent lifestyle diseases such as type II diabetes, cardiovascular disease (heart attack, stroke, high blood pressure and other diseases of the heart and arteries), joint problems and certain forms of cancer. It is suitable for the whole family, adults and children alike – remember that this is the way people around the Mediterranean have traditionally eaten and as a result they have enjoyed a level of good health that is the envy of most other Western nations.

The importance of balanced blood sugar

Balancing the blood sugar through diet is central to my approach – and key to that is choosing the correct carbohydrates. Your body reacts to the food you eat by producing different hormones. Hormonal balance is essential to staying healthy, and two of the most important hormones are insulin and glucagon. Their main task is to regulate the body's blood sugar level. Every time you eat food that contains carbohydrates (like bread, potatoes, rice, pasta, sugar and to a lesser extent vegetables, fruit and pulses) your blood sugar will rise. The pancreas reacts to this by producing insulin. The amount of insulin produced depends on the amount and type of carbohydrate that you eat: carbohydrates that are rapidly absorbed and converted into blood sugar stimulate the release of a high level of insulin; carbohydrates that are absorbed and converted into blood sugar more slowly cause a less pronounced rise in blood sugar and a lower level of insulin in the blood.

One of the most important functions of insulin is to ensure that blood sugar is absorbed from the blood into the cells of the body. It is stored first in the liver and muscles, but if these stores are already full, insulin makes the body store the excess as fat, especially around the waist. Insulin is the energy- and fat-storing hormone of the body.

A high level of insulin in the blood makes it difficult, if not impossible, for the body to burn fat from its fat stores and therefore makes losing weight almost impossible. The same is true if the relationship between insulin and glucagon is unbalanced. Glucagon promotes the burning of body fat to provide energy and when the body is producing glucagon (triggered by the consumption of protein) it is not producing insulin.

The more overweight you are, the more insulin there will be in your blood. The more insulin you have in your blood, the easier it will be to store fat and gain weight.

Besides making it almost impossible to lose weight, too much insulin can also result in long-term damage to your body. The more often your body experiences a high level of insulin, the more difficult it becomes for insulin to lower blood sugar. The pancreas tries to compensate for this by secreting more insulin. The more rapidly-absorbed carbohydrates you consume, the more insulin your body will produce, and as a result you soon become caught in a vicious circle of hyperinsulinaemia (higher insulin production) and reduced insulin sensitivity (insulin resistance). When this happens, your insulin level remains high constantly, whether you have eaten or not. However, it is only the blood-sugar-lowering effect of insulin that has deteriorated. Insulin still continues to promote fat storage. This will result

The benefits

To sum up, the Greek Doctor's Diet means:

▶ normal weight
▶ lower, more stable blood sugar
▶ lower cholesterol and triglycerides
▶ stable mood
▶ normal appetite
▶ fewer inflammatory conditions
▶ mental alertness
▶ increased energy

A typical day with the Greek Doctor's Diet

Breakfast

▶ 2 scrambled eggs, 50 g (1¾ oz) smoked salmon
▶ 1–2 grilled tomatoes sprinkled with
1 teaspoon olive oil

Snack

▶ 125 g (4½ oz) low-fat natural yogurt with 1 kiwi
fruit and 1 tablespoon ground flaxseed

Lunch

▶ 90–150 g (3–5½ oz) cooked chicken mixed with
150 g (5½ oz) cooked chickpeas
▶ mixed rocket and watercress salad with
tomatoes and avocado
▶ 2 tablespoons homemade vinaigrette

Snack

(could be eaten after dinner, if dinner is early)
▶ 1 apple
▶ 10–12 peanuts

Dinner

▶ 250 ml (9 fl oz) broccoli and cauliflower soup
(see page 61)
▶ 125–150 g (4½–5½ oz) red mullet with orange,
ginger and coriander sauce (see page 101)
▶ 200 g (7 oz) steamed mixed vegetables
▶ 100 g (3½ oz) cooked brown rice or couscous

Mastering stress

Stress is something everybody experiences at some time or other. To live in our modern society and be immune to stress is impossible. Each time you experience stress, be it 'positive' or 'negative', your body produces stress hormones. To secure the survival of the species all living creatures have developed protective mechanisms against danger. The 'fight or flight' response allows us to get out of danger fast. Faced with potential danger your heart beats faster, your blood pressure goes up, you may start perspiring and you feel very alert. All this was very helpful for ancient man, who lived in a dangerous environment. If he were faced with a predatory animal, for example, it allowed him to take decisive action and utilize the energy that the fight or flight response provides.

Modern stress, however, rarely has anything to do with real danger. If you experience this sort of stress reaction as a result of being stuck in a traffic jam, for example, you have no opportunity to 'complete' the stress response by using up the energy the stress hormones provide. Experiencing this reaction on a regular basis leads to constantly elevated levels of the stress hormones, adrenalin and cortisol. This sort of chronic stress is one of the major causes of modern lifestyle disorders.

An unhealthy diet can also lead to stress. Why? Because stress hormones are secreted when the blood sugar is unstable, which occurs when you eat high-glycaemic foods. If you eat a baguette or a piece of cake, you will have a sharp and sudden rise in blood sugar. This makes your body increase its production of insulin, which will make your blood sugar level drop about 1½ hours after the meal. The brain, which is dependent on a stable blood sugar level, interprets the falling blood sugar as a danger signal. If your body doesn't intervene, your blood sugar will keep falling and you will pass out. Hence the body starts producing adrenalin and cortisol in order to stabilize the blood sugar at a normal level.

A combination of bad nutrition, lack of exercise, high work pace, poor quality of sleep and lack of relaxation can lead to chronic stress. Chronic stress lowers the chromium level in your body, which leads to higher insulin levels and subsequently an irresistible craving for sweet or starchy food. A chronically elevated insulin level can trigger a wide range of symptoms, including overweight, diabetes, anxiety and depression, fibromyalgia and chronic fatigue syndrome.

You can, however, do something about this. First you have to find the factors that cause you stress and avoid them wherever possible. This is not always easy. None of us is immune to stress, so learning to cope with it is as important as seeking to avoid and reduce it wherever possible. This can be achieved through a combination of stress management techniques (such as tai chi, yoga and meditation) and physical exercise, together with a healthy, well-balanced, low-glycaemic diet.

in weight gain and a greater risk of developing type II diabetes, high cholesterol levels, high blood pressure and cardiovascular disorders, as well as certain types of cancer.

So you can see why it is vital to choose your carbohydrates with care.

How to choose 'slow' carbs

Slow carbs, as their name suggests, are carbohydrates that raise the blood sugar level slowly and therefore do not cause a surge in insulin. The easiest way to determine which carbs are 'slow' is by looking at their Glycaemic Index (GI), though as we will see, it does throw up a few anomalies. GI is a method of ranking carbohydrate foods according to their effect on blood sugar: the faster they are digested and absorbed by the small intestine, the faster and higher the rise in blood sugar, and the higher the GI. Pure glucose can be absorbed directly into the bloodstream, so it has an immediate effect on blood sugar: on a scale of 0 to 100, glucose has a GI of 100.

GI compares food based on equal carbohydrate content, not equal amount of food: 50 g of glucose is pure carbohydrate, whereas the GI for boiled carrot is based on the amount of boiled carrot that contains 50 g of carbs – which is over 650 g (about 1½ lb). Most non-starchy vegetables have a very low carbohydrate content, usually less than 5 per cent. You would therefore need to eat a very large amount of tomatoes or celery, for instance, in order to ingest the 50 g of carbohydrate needed to measure their GI. For this reason, they do not have a GI rating.

Foods that do not contain carbohydrates do not have a direct influence on blood sugar, consequently their GI is zero. This is why there are no GI numbers for foods that consist primarily of protein, such as eggs, chicken, meat and fish. The same is true of foods that consist mainly of fat, such as butter, margarine and oils.

Glycaemic Load – taking GI a step further

It is tempting to take a Glycaemic Index list and say that all food with a high GI is unhealthy and everything with a low GI is good for you. The truth is always more complicated. GI is by no means the only health measure. If it were, margarine, with a GI of 0, would be very healthy, but that is not the case. Furthermore, you cannot say that banana and mango are bad for you, even though their GI is relatively high.

If we concentrate solely on what is good or bad for your blood sugar – ignoring vitamins, minerals and fat for the moment – the amount of carbohydrates eaten is clearly important. However, the GI is a measure of how fast the carbohydrate in any given food raises blood sugar; it says nothing about the amount of carbohydrate in the food, i.e. how much of it you would need to eat to elicit the response suggested by its GI. Remember, the level of insulin produced is based on the amount of carbs as well as how fast they are converted to blood sugar.

Researchers from Harvard University have therefore come up with the Glycaemic Load (GL). The GL is, in the same way as the GI, an index ranking foods according to their effect on blood sugar. However, while GI gives us information on how fast blood sugar rises after we eat 50 g of digestible carbohydrate in various foods, the GL takes into account both the GI and the amount of carbohydrate in 100 g of food, or a given portion. It therefore gives a far more accurate assessment of foods, because it reflects the effect on the blood sugar of a specific portion of a food.

The use of the GL principle has meant that a number of foods previously blacklisted (as far as their effect on blood sugar was concerned) under the GI system now appear in a far more favourable light. Watermelon is a good example. It has a GI of 72 because the type of carbohydrate it contains was found to raise blood sugar rapidly. However, since it contains very little of that carbohydrate its GL per 100 g is only 4.

At the back of the book you will find a chart listing both the GI and GL of many common foods.

As I stated earlier, this diet is all about restoring a natural balance of the carbohydrates, protein and fats that you eat. Having looked at carbohydrates, let's turn our attention to protein and fats – two essential components of a healthy diet.

Protein

Protein is crucial to our bodies. Our cells, hormones and immune system are all based on and communicate through proteins, so obviously we must ensure that we get enough of this vital nutrient. Proteins are made up of smaller compounds called amino acids, of which there are about 20 different kinds. Eleven of these can be produced by the human body. The remaining nine cannot be produced in the body, therefore they have to be provided by the food we eat. These are called 'essential amino acids'. If we do not get enough essential amino acids, our bodily functions will deteriorate.

There are two sources of protein: animal protein and plant protein. Animal protein is found in milk and other dairy products, eggs, all meats, poultry, fish and shellfish. Note that it is the saturated fat in dairy products and meat that are less healthy in large quantities, not the protein. If you choose lean meats and low-fat dairy products, fat is not an issue. Plant protein is mainly found in nuts, pulses such as beans, lentils and chickpeas and, to a lesser extent, in vegetables. For guidelines on choosing healthy sources of protein, see pages 31–39.

It is absolutely essential that you eat enough protein. Too little protein can lead to loss of lean body mass, or muscle. Muscles, large and small, are important for movement and because they protect our vital inner organs. The muscles also constitute

the part of the body that burns the most energy; so less muscle mass means a slower metabolism. Many age-related illnesses are linked to the loss of muscle. Many protein foods are also a source of important vitamins and minerals, so a low intake may result in a lack of antioxidants produced by the body – and these are part of our defence against premature ageing and illness.

Protein's role in metabolism

Protein is a key element for an efficient metabolism, and our consumption of protein has an effect on a number of hormones. Most importantly, protein stimulates production of the growth hormone IGF-1 and the hormone glucagon. The growth hormone increases muscle mass, while glucagon promotes the burning of body fat to provide energy. Glucagon's main function is to increase blood sugar if it is falling (for instance, during fasting or between meals), thus ensuring a steady energy supply for the body. Blood sugar is released from the liver's sugar supply (glycogen) and is also produced from proteins and fat. When the body is producing glucagon the effect is less fat storage and more burning of body fat.

Let me emphasize that this is not a high-protein diet. The amount of protein I recommend (see page 21) is somewhat higher than most of us are used to (at the expense of carbohydrates), but the total amount is not high.

Fats

Nothing is as important to our health as eating the right kind of fat. The low rates of heart disease and other such conditions in those eating a traditional Mediterranean diet, where olive oil plays a central role, is testament to that. So, as with carbohydrates and protein, the key is to choose your source wisely.

In food, fat is found in the form of triglycerides. When digested, these triglycerides are split into their components: glycerol and three fatty acids.

Nature contains numerous fatty acids, but only some play an important role in nutrition.

A number of fatty acids are important because they are building blocks for substances that are part of our immune system and have a positive influence on inflammatory reactions. Others are vital to a well-functioning metabolism, because we need the right kind of fat from our food in order to burn fat. Obese individuals often lack essential fatty acids, or the relationship between the types of fat they eat is wrong, and they have too much stored saturated fat (either originating directly from the diet or converted from excess carbohydrate). In combination with antioxidants, fatty acids influence our defence mechanisms against cancer, while others are important in preventing illnesses such as diabetes and heart disease. So, you see, there's more to fat than meets the eye.

All fats contain both saturated and unsaturated fatty acids, but are usually described as saturated or unsaturated, depending on the proportions of fatty acids present. Butter, for instance, is usually thought of as a saturated fat because it contains 60–65 per cent saturated and 30–35 per cent unsaturated fat. Within the unsaturated category are two types of fats – monounsaturated and polyunsaturated. The human body is able to produce saturated and monounsaturated fatty acids, but not some types of polyunsaturated fatty acids. Some of these, however, are essential for good health; the only way we can obtain these is through our diet. These are called essential fatty acids, usually referred to as omega-3 and omega-6. These fatty acids are an integral part of all cell membranes. The brain and nervous system consist mainly of these essential fatty acids, and depression and many disorders of the nervous system are linked to a low intake of omega-3 fatty acids. Western diets are generally too high in omega-6 and too low in omega-3 and this imbalance promotes chronic inflammation, which is the cause of many painful and life-threatening disorders.

You will find more guidance on fats in the section on 'Ingredients for good health' – see pages 44–45.

Exercise for better health

The Greek Doctor's Diet concept is not just about what you eat. Exercise is essential for good health and a combination of the Greek Doctor's Diet, regular exercise and a healthier lifestyle in general will give you the best results, whether your aim is to lose weight or simply stay as healthy as you possibly can.

Many people believe that you need to do strenuous exercise if you want to lose weight and be in good health. This is not correct. Without a change in diet, the weight loss that will result from exercise alone is small. Moreover, it is not necessary to train very hard to gain positive health effects. The crucial thing is to turn a form of exercise that you enjoy into a part of your everyday life: you don't have to 'spin' yourself to death on an exercise bike. It is better to exercise moderately, but daily. Walking for at least 20–30 minutes every day and strength training the major muscle groups (especially the thighs) 2–3 times a week is adequate for many people, when combined with a healthy diet.

Human beings are designed to move in order to get food. During the Stone Age we would have walked an average of 30 km a day to find food – sometimes unsuccessfully. If we got something to eat, the important thing was to stay put and not use energy unnecessarily – until we got hungry again. This is the reason why it makes sense to exercise early in the day and on an empty stomach. It goes well with our hormones and biorhythms. When we get up in the morning, the carbohydrate store in the liver is nearly empty, the blood pressure is relatively low and the insulin level is at its lowest. Low insulin means that the body can more easily burn stored fat as fuel. Remember that a high level of insulin means fat storage whereas low insulin means that fat can be burnt efficiently.

If you can't get up early enough to fit in a session, try finding ways of exercising on your way to work.

Perhaps you could walk or cycle to work. Or you could get off the bus a couple of stops earlier and get a brisk 20–30 minute walk. Exercising early in the day every day is simply the best gift you can give yourself and your metabolism. That said, any exercise, irrespective of the time of day you do it, is clearly better than none at all. In fact, being physically inactive is a much greater health hazard than being overweight. You can be 'fit fat' and reduce the risk of most diseases by exercising on a regular basis. Sadly, being both physically inactive and overweight is not uncommon, and this increases your health risks even more.

What should I eat before and after exercising?

Avoid carbohydrates, especially high-glycaemic foods, before you exercise as this increases the levels of blood sugar and insulin, and decreases fat burning. However, after tough (not moderate) exercise eating high-glycaemic food will help you recover more quickly.

Remember that you will get the most out of exercising if you provide your body with an appropriate amount of protein. Exercise stimulates the production of growth hormones that build more muscle, but only if there are enough 'bricks', i.e. proteins. Ideally, you should drink a large glass of water and have some low-glycaemic fruit as soon as you get up and then exercise for 20–30 minutes. To maximize the effect of morning exercise, especially weight training, have 15–20 g of protein (for instance yogurt or cottage cheese) shortly before starting the exercise or no later than 1–1½ hours afterwards. This increases the production of glucagon and growth hormone, thereby enhancing muscle tissue and fat burning. After exercising, you should eat a well-balanced breakfast, treating it as a main meal (see next page).

Basic diet principles

Technically I call my diet the isoglycaemic diet (*isos* is the Greek word for 'equal'): it is all about balance. The aim is to restore a more natural balance of the types of carbohydrates, proteins and fats you eat.

You will be eating fewer refined and processed foods and a greater range of natural foods – those that suit you genetically and that will improve your metabolism. Nothing is banned (I'm just being realistic), but if you eat less favourable carbs and fats, do so in moderation and balance their effect with a greater intake of healthy carbs and proteins.

Approximately one-third of your total energy intake (by which I mean calories, not amount of food) should come from low- and medium-glycaemic carbohydrates: these are carbohydrates that don't make your blood sugar rise rapidly. Less than one-third should come from high-quality animal and plant proteins, and the rest from minimally processed natural fat, primarily monounsaturated and polyunsaturated fats, but also, to a lesser degree, saturated fats. Sounds too much like

science? Don't worry, you will not need to count grams, percentages or calories. In fact, you will not need to count or weigh anything at all; the palm of your hand is all you need to judge the amount of food you should eat, as I'll explain shortly.

Here's the ABC of the Greek Doctor's Diet: most of your meals will consist of approximately one-third protein foods (part A of the 'plate model' opposite) and two-thirds low-glycaemic carbohydrates (part B of the 'plate model'). One meal a day – your 'reward' meal – may consist of one-third protein, half low-glycaemic carbohydrates and one-sixth (part C) medium- or high-glycaemic carbohydrates. You can choose whether to have this for breakfast, lunch or dinner. To be in tune with human metabolic biorhythm, it is probably best to have your reward meal as your breakfast or lunch, but many people will choose dinner, for practical and social reasons.

Fat does not appear on the plate models because it is needed in smaller amounts. It is often 'hidden' as part of food preparation, or in sauces or salad dressings. The best fats are the

The Greek Doctor's Diet food triangle

A simple way to visualize this way of eating is to use a food triangle. As you can see, the base of the triangle consists of vegetables and pulses with a low GL. Fruit with a low GL also comes into this category. These foods (see page 39) make up the B part of your meals.

Higher up, you will find foods rich in protein and unsaturated fat. These make up the A part of your meals.

Near the top are high-glycaemic carbohydrates (mainly starchy and sweet foods). These constitute the C part of your once-a-day reward meal.

	Saturated fat: butter, cheese
C *High GL*	*Sugar, white bread, white flour, potatoes*
A *GL-regulating*	*Unsaturated fat: extra virgin olive oil, avocado oil, nuts and seeds, oily fish*
C *Medium–high GL*	*Durum wheat pasta, non-sticky rice, e.g. basmati, long-grain, wholegrain products, dense bread made from less processed grains*
A *GL-regulating*	*Protein: fish, chicken, lean meat, game, eggs, yogurt, cottage cheese*
B *Low GL*	*Vegetables, pulses, low-glycaemic fruit*

unsaturated types found in extra virgin olive oil, nuts, cold-pressed nut oils, avocados, oily fish and flaxseed oil. Limit your intake of saturated fat (mainly found in animal sources such as butter, cheese and meat).

Water is the best 'health drink': 2 litres (3½ pints) is a minimum for most adults. A glass of wine with your lunch or dinner is fine in terms of health – but if you are trying to lose weight I would recommend that you avoid alcohol or that you use it as the C part of your reward meal.

You may eat almost as much as you want until you feel comfortably full (do not eat too quickly as it takes 10–15 minutes for satiety signals to reach the brain), but you must always balance what you eat. If you want a second helping, that's fine, but don't just eat more carbohydrates. You should eat a corresponding (smaller) amount of protein. No meal or snack should be without protein.

How much should I eat?

Without weighing and measuring, the diagrams opposite will help you to envisage what your meals will look like. For an adult, the amount of protein food should be about as big and thick as the palm of your hand. Palm size varies from one person to another and is proportionate with the rest of the body. This is the amount of protein-based food (cooked and ready to eat) that you need, and it constitutes the A part of each of your three main meals per day.

The B part (mainly vegetables and pulses, as well as low-glycaemic fruits and berries) should be twice as big as the protein part: two palms.

The C part of the reward meal should not be bigger than half a palm, and the B part should not be reduced to less than one and a half palms. Part C also includes dessert and cheese or wine/alcohol.

Snacks should be about half to one-third the size of main meals, keeping otherwise to the proportions.

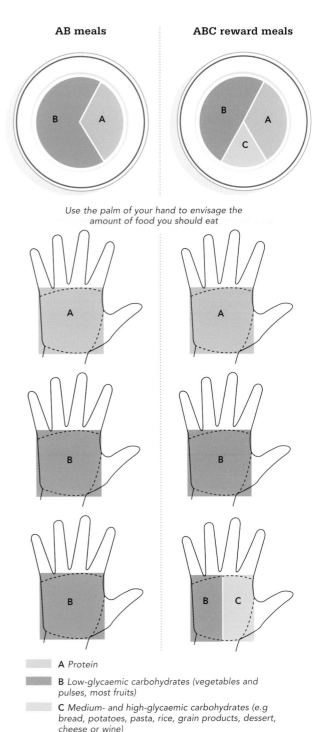

AB meals   **ABC reward meals**

Use the palm of your hand to envisage the amount of food you should eat

A *Protein*

B *Low-glycaemic carbohydrates (vegetables and pulses, most fruits)*

C *Medium- and high-glycaemic carbohydrates (e.g bread, potatoes, pasta, rice, grain products, dessert, cheese or wine)*

What can I eat?

Pulses

1 to 3 servings per day
1 serving = 150 g (5½ oz)

▶ Beans
▶ Chickpeas
▶ Dried peas
▶ Lentils

Vegetables

Unlimited amount
▶ Artichokes
▶ Asparagus
▶ Aubergines (eggplants)
▶ Bamboo shoots
▶ Bean sprouts
▶ Broccoli
▶ Brussels sprouts
▶ Cabbage, all kinds
▶ Cauliflower
▶ Celery
▶ Courgettes (zucchini)
▶ Cucumber
▶ Fennel
▶ Green beans
▶ Green peas
▶ Leeks
▶ Onions, garlic
▶ Pak choi (bok choy)
▶ Peppers (capsicums)
▶ Radishes
▶ Salad leaves
   (e.g. lettuce, chicory, rocket)
▶ Spinach
▶ Spring onions
▶ Tomatoes
▶ Watercress

Fruit

2 servings per day
1 serving = 1 whole fruit unless otherwise indicated or 100 g (3½ oz) berries, cherries or grapes

▶ Apple
▶ Apricots (3)
▶ Berries, all kinds
▶ Cherries
▶ Grapefruit
▶ Grapes
▶ Kiwi fruit (1–2)
▶ Melon
▶ Nectarine
▶ Orange
▶ Peach
▶ Pear
▶ Plum
▶ Pomegranate
▶ Passion fruit (2)
▶ Tangerines (2)
▶ Watermelon (up to 200 g/7 oz serving)

Protein sources

**3 to 5 servings per day, of which at least
1 serving is fish**
1 serving = 90–200 g (3–7 oz) prepared;
approximately 120–180 g (4–6 oz) raw

▶ Eggs (1 serving = 2–3 whole eggs or 5 whites)
▶ Fish (preferably oily fish), shellfish
▶ Chicken breast, turkey breast
▶ Game (venison, rabbit, pheasant, etc.)
▶ Lean meat from lamb, beef or pork
▶ Cottage cheese (150 g/5½ oz serving)
▶ Tofu (100 g/3½ oz serving)

Root vegetables

1 to 2 servings per day
1 serving = 100 g (3½ oz) boiled, 200 g (7 oz) raw

- ▶ Beetroot
- ▶ Carrots
- ▶ Celeriac
- ▶ Jerusalem artichokes
- ▶ Sweet potato

Fat sources

1 to 3 tbs per day, divided among all meals

- ▶ Extra virgin olive oil or rapeseed (canola) oil
- ▶ Sesame oil
- ▶ Homemade mayonnaise made with extra virgin olive oil
- ▶ Half an avocado

Nuts and seeds

1 to 3 servings per day
1 serving = 15 g/½ oz

- ▶ 10–12 almonds, cashew nuts, peanuts or hazelnuts
- ▶ 6–8 walnut halves
- ▶ 4 macadamia nuts
- ▶ 2 Brazil nuts
- ▶ 2 tbs sesame, sunflower, pumpkin or flax seeds

Dairy products

1 serving per day

- ▶ 125 g (4½ oz) fat-free or low-fat natural (unsweetened) yogurt
- ▶ 250 ml (8 fl oz) skimmed or semi-skimmed milk
- ▶ 250 ml (8 fl oz) soya milk

Coarse grain products

1 serving per day
1 serving = 100 g (3½ oz) boiled grains, 3 tbs cereal, or 1 slice of wholegrain bread

- ▶ Brown basmati rice
- ▶ Wild rice
- ▶ Oats
- ▶ Barley
- ▶ Couscous
- ▶ Quinoa
- ▶ Buckwheat
- ▶ High-fibre, wholegrain cereal or unsweetened muesli (preferably without dried fruit)
- ▶ Wholewheat or protein-enriched/low-carb pasta
- ▶ Very dark wholegrain bread (such as pumpernickel) or soya and linseed bread

Taste enhancers

Unlimited amount

- ▶ Dijon mustard
- ▶ Vinegar (all kinds)
- ▶ Herbs
- ▶ Spices
- ▶ Chillies
- ▶ Tabasco and other hot-pepper sauces
- ▶ Lemon and lime juice
- ▶ Grated fresh horseradish

Beverages

Unlimited amount

- ▶ Water (at least 8 glasses a day)
- ▶ Decaffeinated coffee or decaffeinated tea (if desired, use a non-caloric sweetener)
- ▶ Green tea

Sample menu plans

This two-week menu plan provides an example of how the Greek Doctor's Diet might work in practice. Its purpose is to provide inspiration to help you get started on a new way of eating. There is no need to follow it strictly; rather, think of it as a guide to help you break away from your current eating habits and choose the path to good health. All of us have different daily routines so you will undoubtedly need to adapt these meal suggestions to your circumstances: if, for example, you work in an office with no facilities to heat food for lunch then you can still enjoy the convenience of a soup that you have made in advance, but you will need to heat it up before you leave home and put it in a thermos flask; in contrast, if you work from home you will be able to enjoy many more freshly-cooked hot meals at lunchtime.

Please note that the times indicated for each meal are there to make sure that you eat often enough. Obviously you may adjust them to suit your own schedule.

It can be difficult to change food habits on your own, so it is important that you seek support from those close to you. It is also vital – if you do not do the shopping or cooking – that the person preparing food at home is willing to help you. Besides, a healthy diet is good for the whole family!

The following tips should help you either adapt these menu plans to your needs, or devise your own, while still fulfilling the general guidelines of the diet.

▶ Cooking food in advance is a great way to save time and effort. Whenever you cook a meal that can be chilled or frozen, make extra portions and freeze or store for later use – either as a lunch, or a main course on nights when you don't have the time or inclination to cook. I cannot overestimate the value of coming home after a long day and being able to enjoy a healthy, homemade meal that requires no effort. The menu plans on the following pages include a number of soups and main courses that can be prepared in advance – these are indicated by an asterisk.

▶ The suggested amounts are meant only as a guideline. Feel free to increase them if necessary, so that you feel pleasantly full, but make sure that each meal is properly balanced, following the AB or ABC plate model (see page 21).

▶ Variety is vital. Mindlessly eating the same foods day after day is a sure path to weight gain, and diets that restrict your choice of foods are difficult to stick to for very long. But there's more to it than that. Many vitamins and minerals work best in combination with other micronutrients, and eating a variety of foods will ensure you get a good mix of micronutrients.

▶ Make sure that you have some protein-rich food (fish, poultry, egg, milk, cottage cheese, yogurt, tofu) with every meal and snack, in order to obtain the best possible glycaemic effect.

▶ Cottage cheese, fromage frais and quark are all good, low-fat sources of protein. For variety, add fresh berries, chopped nuts, spices and fresh herbs.

▶ Plain, natural yogurt is another good source of protein. If you're trying to lose weight, look for fat-free natural yogurt – it tastes just as good as the regular type. Avoid fruit-flavoured yogurts, as most are loaded with sugar. Opt for sugar-free alternatives, if available.

▶ A squeeze of fresh lemon juice over cooked vegetables, salads, fish and shellfish, and even some poultry and meat dishes, reduces the glycaemic effect and adds a wonderful fresh taste of the Mediterranean.

▶ Many meals and snacks benefit from the addition of a teaspoon of flaxseed oil just before you eat them: this gives you the benefits of omega-3 fats and reduces the glycaemic effect of your meal.

Menu plan week 1

	7am Breakfast	10am Snack
Monday	small bowl unsweetened muesli (C) 1 tbs ground flaxseed 250 ml (8 fl oz) skimmed milk 100 g (3½ oz) berries	100–150 g (3½–5½ oz) cottage cheese 1 tbs pumpkin seeds
Tuesday	2 scrambled eggs mushrooms (cooked with 1 tsp olive oil)	125 g (4½ oz) natural yogurt 100 g (3½ oz) fresh berries
Wednesday	small bowl mixed fruit salad 125 g (4½ oz) natural yogurt 2 tbs mixed chopped nuts	100–150 g (3½–5½ oz) cottage cheese 75 g (2½ oz) prawns dill
Thursday	2 boiled eggs 1 slice soya and linseed bread (C) 1–2 tbs cottage cheese 1 peach or nectarine	1 apple 10 almonds
Friday	small bowl porridge (C) 1 tbs ground flaxseed 1 grated apple	125 g (4½ oz) natural yogurt 1–2 tbs sunflower or pumpkin seeds 1 pear
Saturday	½ small orange-fleshed melon 1 slice pumpernickel bread (C) 2–3 tbs cottage cheese 150 g (5½ oz) prawns	1 kiwi fruit 10 hazelnuts
Sunday	½–1 grapefruit 2 eggs (cooked in 1 tsp olive oil) 100–150 g (3½–5½ oz) smoked mackerel 1–2 tomatoes, grilled	1 apple 2 Brazil nuts

The numbers in parentheses refer to the page numbers of the recipes in this book.
The letter (C) is a suggestion for the C part of your ABC reward meal.
* indicates that the dish is a 'make ahead' recipe

12.30pm Lunch	4pm Snack	7pm Dinner
–200 g (3½–7 oz) grilled icken or turkey breast ed leaf salad with artichoke hearts, ives and 1 tbs grated Parmesan	1 pear 10 almonds	hummus and crudités *salmon fishcakes (94) stir-fried green vegetables
–150 g (3½–5½ oz) noked mackerel ket and avocado salad ice pumpernickel bread (C)	100 g (3½ oz) grapes 2 Brazil nuts	chicken, walnut and red bean salad (77)
eek vegetable soup (60)	2–3 tsp natural peanut butter celery sticks	grilled trout avocado, courgette and pasta salad (C) (80) green salad

ned sardines in olive oil, mixed with
hopped red pepper (capsicum),
elery, spring onion, lemon juice and
tsp mayonnaise, on crisp lettuce
	125 g (4½ oz) natural yogurt
	4 walnut halves
	30–40 g (1–1¼ oz) plain dark chocolate
	   (70 % cocoa solids)
		100–200 g (3½–7 oz) cold ham or turkey
		   tomato salad with beans and basil (77)
		watercress salad

arinated prawns (94) ed green salad	100–150 g (3½–5½ oz) cottage cheese 4 cherry tomatoes fresh basil	*chickpea fritters (137) Greek salad (82)
ssels with white beans nd olives (89) amed green beans	aubergine purée (85) raw carrot and red pepper (capsicum)	*stuffed peppers (122) green salad with vinaigrette raspberry yogurt sorbet (150)
ushroom soup with oats' cheese (64)	8 olives 10 almonds	*pork casserole with chickpeas and orange (120) 100 g (3½ oz) cooked couscous (C) steamed broccoli and mangetouts

Menu plan week 2

	7am Breakfast	10am Snack
Monday	3 tbs All-Bran (C) 1 tbs ground flaxseed 250 ml (8 fl oz) skimmed milk $\frac{1}{2}$–1 grapefruit	100–150 g ($3\frac{1}{2}$–$5\frac{1}{2}$ oz) cottage cheese chopped red pepper (capsicum), car and courgette (zucchini)
Tuesday	2 scrambled eggs 50 g ($1\frac{3}{4}$ oz) smoked salmon cherry tomatoes 1 kiwi fruit	1 apple 2 Brazil nuts
Wednesday	small bowl mixed fruit salad 125 g ($4\frac{1}{2}$ oz) natural yogurt 2 tbs chopped nuts	grated carrot 1 tbs sunflower or sesame seeds 1 tsp olive oil or sesame oil
Thursday	3 tbs unsweetened muesli (C) 1 tbs sunflower seeds 250 ml (8 fl oz) skimmed milk 100 g ($3\frac{1}{2}$ oz) berries	2–3 tsp natural peanut butter celery sticks
Friday	3 slices ham 2 poached eggs grilled mushrooms	100 g ($3\frac{1}{2}$ oz) grapes 2 Brazil nuts
Saturday	small bowl porridge (C) 1 tbs ground flaxseed 1 kiwi fruit 125 g ($4\frac{1}{2}$ oz) natural yogurt	125 g ($4\frac{1}{2}$ oz) cottage cheese 100 g ($3\frac{1}{2}$ oz) berries
Sunday	2 eggs (cooked in 1 tsp olive oil) 2 slices lean bacon 1–2 tomatoes, grilled	1 pear 6–8 walnut halves

12.30pm Lunch	4pm Snack	7pm Dinner
rk casserole with chickpeas and ange (120)	100 g (3½ oz) grapes 10 almonds	*lemon-marinated sardines (96) watercress, tomato and avocado salad
ushroom soup with goats' cheese (64)	2–3 tsp natural peanut butter carrot sticks	chicken kebabs with fresh herbs (109) basmati rice with nuts (C) (145) tomato salad with beans and basil (77) green salad
a, chickpea and avocado salad (74)	100–150 g (3½–5½ oz) cottage cheese 4 cherry tomatoes	meat mixture from *stuffed peppers (122) 100 g (3½ oz) cooked pasta (C) steamed mixed vegetables
g (5½ oz) prawns mixed with 1 tbs omage frais, 1 tsp tomato purée aste), lemon juice and coriander ercress salad	1 orange 4 macadamia nuts	100–200 g (3½–7 oz) grilled chicken or turkey breast black beans with herbs (141) courgette and mushroom gratin (129)
ng bean and tomato salad (142) range or 2 satsumas	2–3 tbs hummus raw cauliflower, carrot and red pepper (capsicum)	swordfish with garlic and walnut sauce (98) steamed green beans 100 g (3½ oz) cooked brown rice (C)
mon fishcakes (94) en salad with avocado	8 olives 10 almonds	courgette and fennel omelette (131) Puy lentils with red wine (141)
hite beans with tomatoes (140) –150 g (3½–5½ oz) prawns, grilled	tzatziki (87) carrot and celery sticks	*lamb with apricots and almonds (118) herbed quinoa pilaf (C) (144) steamed spinach baked apples with vanilla sauce (154)

Ingredients for
good health

This chapter looks at the various foods that help optimize health. There are more than 100 trillion cells in the human body, and in each cell there are thousands of biochemical reactions every second, every day throughout our lives. Food is involved in all of these reactions. Unfortunately, today's highly processed food rarely supplies us with everything we need to be truly healthy. It provides the energy to survive and function on a day-to-day basis, but it leaves a lot to be desired if we want optimum health and vitality. Much of the food we eat consists of empty, useless calories, with ingredients that have been processed beyond recognition.

Our vitality and our ability to maintain or restore good health are totally dependent on our lifestyle and diet. You need food that gives you nourishment, not just energy. But food should also nourish you in another way – it should be a positive and enjoyable aspect of your life, something to look forward to; something that will boost your family and social life. Food should be exciting and creative. The healthy, delicious ingredients and recipes that form the basis of the Greek Doctor's Diet will ensure that eating well becomes a natural part of your life.

In the previous section I outlined the ABC system of the Greek Doctor's Diet and provided some guidance on what you should eat. Here, I'll look at those foods in more detail, starting with the A part of the diet, which consists of foods that provide protein, such as fish, poultry, meat, game, eggs and dairy products.

Protein

Protein is very important in relation to the Greek Doctor's Diet because, by stimulating the production of the metabolism-boosting hormone glucagon, it regulates the production of insulin. The effect of this is to stabilize blood sugar. Protein will generally lower the glycaemic effect of a meal, which is important for everybody who wishes to have stable blood sugar, and particularly for those who are overweight or diabetic.

Most people get the bulk of the protein they need from eating fish and shellfish, chicken and other poultry, various types of meat, eggs, dairy products, nuts, and also pulses, especially soya bean products. Protein is made up of 20 amino acids, nine of which cannot be produced in the body and need to be provided by our diet. However, all protein foods are not created equal: they contain varying amounts of these amino acids. The best composition of amino acids for the human body comes from animal sources such as meat, fish, poultry and eggs.

Many vegetables and grains also contain protein, but vegetable sources of protein are generally lacking in one or more amino acids, so in order to obtain the full complement of protein from these sources, it is necessary to combine incomplete sources of protein, for instance pulses and grains. Soya beans are an exception as they provide a full and well-balanced mixture of essential amino acids – and are therefore a valuable and healthy protein for vegetarians and meat eaters alike. Spirulina (a type of algae) is another good protein source from the plant world.

Those who eat seafood and meat have a far greater choice of proteins – but some are healthier than others.

Fish and shellfish

If you are searching for a source of healthy protein, start with fish and shellfish. They contain a multitude of vitamins and minerals, especially B-vitamins and minerals such as selenium, iodine, zinc, phosphorus and copper. Iodine is very important to the body's production of the hormone thyroxin, which influences metabolism. Shellfish is a particularly good source of zinc and selenium. Oysters are perhaps nature's best source of zinc, a mineral that is crucial for cell growth and repair, a strong immune system, brain function, eyesight and reproduction (sperm motility as well as potency).

Fatty fish such as salmon, trout, mackerel, sardines and tuna contain essential omega-3 fatty acids and are at the same time a good source of the fat-soluble vitamins A, D and E. The hugely beneficial omega-3 fatty acids lower triglycerides (fatty substances in the blood) and enhance insulin sensitivity, resulting in lower insulin levels in the blood and less insulin resistance. Both these effects lead to lower blood pressure and help to prevent heart disease. Omega-3 fatty acids also have a series of other health benefits, both because they form part of the structure of all our body's cells and because they contribute to the production of favourable anti-inflammatory substances.

How often should we eat fish and shellfish? As often as you can, but at least twice a week, especially oily fish. The only proviso is that you limit your intake of the larger oily fish such as tuna and swordfish, due to concerns about the toxins they may contain. These large fish eat smaller fish and live longer so they are more likely to accumulate toxins such as mercury; smaller fish such as sardines are less likely to be contaminated to the same extent. Pregnant women are advised to avoid shark, marlin and swordfish and limit their intake of fresh and canned tuna. I advise pregnant women to eat plenty of white fish and to get their omega-3 fatty acids from high-quality supplements.

Vary your choice of fish – and don't forget shellfish. Prawns, langoustines, scallops, squid, mussels and clams taste delicious and are quick to cook. At one time some shellfish were thought to raise cholesterol levels but scientists have now rejected this theory.

Canned seafood is another healthy choice; and it is convenient and good value. Opt for varieties canned in olive oil or springwater – but avoid those canned in sunflower or other vegetable oil.

Chicken and other poultry

One of the great advantages of poultry, regardless of type, is that most of the fat, between 50 and 85 per cent, is in the skin. The meat itself is fairly lean. By removing the skin you will get lean protein of very high quality. Poultry contains plenty of B-vitamins and is also rich in zinc, magnesium and iron. The darker parts, such as the legs, contain more iron than the lighter parts, which on the other hand are quite rich in magnesium. And did you know that duck contains more iron than beef?

The leanest poultry is turkey. Its low fat content means it is very important to use low temperatures when you cook whole turkey or turkey joints. By doing so you will retain the natural juices in the meat, and the result will be a succulent dish with no need for rich sauces to compensate for dry meat. Both chicken and turkey can be minced to form the basis of a wide variety of low-fat dishes.

Pork, veal, bacon and ham

Pork and veal are good sources of protein – as long as you choose lean cuts, such as fillet (tenderloin), medallions or escalopes, and trim off any visible fat. Both meats have excellent nutritional profiles. They contain considerable amounts of minerals such as potassium, zinc and phosphorous. Pork is particularly rich in vitamins B1 (thiamin), B12 and iron (iron from meat is absorbed by the body five times more efficiently than iron from plant sources); veal is a good source of the B-group vitamins and folic acid.

Fat enhances the flavour of meat and prevents it becoming dry when it is cooked, so it is important to compensate for this when you prepare lean cuts of veal or pork. Marinating in olive oil and lemon juice – with garlic and herbs if you like – will give a very tasty and juicy result. You can also choose to fry the meat in olive oil at a low temperature.

If you like bacon, buy lean back bacon rather than streaky, trim off the fat before cooking and enjoy it

as an occasional treat rather than every day. Lean ham is a tasty addition to salads and any fat can easily be trimmed off.

Beef and lamb

These red meats are not a regular feature of the traditional healthy Mediterranean diet. They were mainly served on special occasions – and certainly not eaten three or four times a week, as many people now seem to do. But why has red meat, such as beef and lamb, acquired such a bad reputation from the point of view of health?

It is the saturated fat content that originally sparked off concerns. An excess of saturated fat in the diet, combined with a lack of exercise, contributes to a higher level of LDL cholesterol (the 'bad' form of cholesterol) in the blood. As LDL cholesterol passes through the arteries it can become trapped in lesions on the artery walls, creating a fatty plaque. Here, the cholesterol is prone to damage (oxidation). Smoking, stress, a low intake of antioxidants (found mainly in vegetables, nuts, pulses, fruits and berries) and a high intake of high-glycaemic carbohydrates have all been shown to increase oxidation in the body. An elevated cholesterol level by itself is probably not enough to make you predisposed to heart problems. It is when the LDL cholesterol is oxidized that it can lead to heart disease. The trans fatty acids in hydrogenated fats (found in margarines and in many ready-made foods, from breakfast cereals and soups to cakes, biscuits, pies and other pastry products) have a much more harmful effect than saturated fat.

OK, so red meat is not the worst thing you can eat by any means. However, aside from its saturated fat content, there is another reason not to eat it too often. The saturated fat in red meat (and also in egg yolks) contains arachidonic acid, an omega-6 fatty acid. An excess of this fatty acid causes the formation of inflammatory substances that can lead to high blood pressure, an increased tendency to blood coagulation and risk of thrombosis, as well as various inflammatory conditions such as chronic fatigue, arthritis and flaky skin.

Is there anything positive to be said for red meat? Of course there is. It tastes fantastic and contains protein of excellent quality, along with B-vitamins and important minerals such as iron and zinc. Personally, I do not eat red meat often, because I prefer fish, chicken and turkey. That does not mean I never eat red meat. When I do, I choose the best and leanest parts, such as fillet of beef or leg of lamb.

When using minced meat, I always pick a good piece of meat with no fat and ask the butcher to mince it for me. You can do this quite easily yourself, using a food processor. This way you will be sure that the meat is lean. Pre-packed minced meat can contain quite a lot of fat (and ice water that you pay a high price for).

One red meat you may not have considered is ostrich. It is very tasty, tender and extremely lean. It has a taste somewhere between beef and lamb, and is as lean as venison. It is now being farmed more widely so it is becoming more easily available.

Game

Game is some of the healthiest meat you can eat. It is low in fat and high in iron, and if you buy a wild specimen, as opposed to farmed game, it will have had a significantly better diet and way of life than most chickens, cows and pigs.

The fat also contains a somewhat higher level of omega-3 fatty acids than regular red meat.

Now that venison is farmed it has become more popular and widely available. Hare and wild rabbit are also good choices though they are not always readily available. Game birds such as pheasant, partridge and wild duck are also a good choice of protein. Young birds can be roasted in no time but older birds are somewhat tougher and need to be roasted slowly or cooked in a casserole.

Eggs

All eggs are a valuable source of protein, and eggs from poultry that live in a free and natural way are a rich source of other nutrients, including vitamin B12. Just like other animals, what the hens have been allowed to eat will influence the nutritional content of the eggs. This is especially true of the fat quality. If the hens do not get favourable omega-3 fatty acids through their natural diet, there will be little of it in the egg yolk. When buying eggs, try to find free-range eggs from a local farm; these are sold in some supermarkets.

At one time there were health concerns about the cholesterol content of eggs. However, several studies have now established that eating eggs has no bearing on the level of cholesterol in the blood. As I mentioned above, eggs, like beef, do contain arachidonic acid, a fatty acid that can cause health problems if the level in the blood gets too high or for those who are sensitive to it. The major symptoms of sensitivity to, or an elevated level of, arachidonic acid are chronic exhaustion, poor sleep quality, problems getting out of bed in the morning, thin or fine hair, thin nails, indigestion, dry flaky skin and rashes.

Dairy products

Dairy products, though not essential for good health, are a source of high-quality protein and several important vitamins and minerals, including B-vitamins and calcium. Unfortunately, some dairy foods are also high in saturated fat. Your best choices of dairy proteins are natural, unsweetened yogurt and cottage cheese – both of which are an important part of my diet. Fromage frais and quark are alternatives to cottage cheese: all are low in saturated fat, but choose natural products, not sweetened, fruit-flavoured versions.

On the whole, you should avoid high-fat cheeses, though I do not recommend that you eat processed reduced-fat cheeses instead. If you are a cheese-lover, enjoy an occasional piece of high-fat cheese as a treat, and serve it with fruit or salad, not with high-glycaemic carbohydrates. A lot of cheese in combination with bread, crackers, or on pizza, is one of the reasons many people are overweight. I use small amounts of feta and Parmesan in salads and cooked vegetable dishes: with these strongly flavoured cheeses, a little goes a long way.

I am not a great fan of milk – it contains a significant amount of the sugar lactose and, being a liquid, does not offer the same level of satiety as solid dairy foods. If you like milk, choose skimmed milk or semi-skimmed, or try soya milk, which is a good alternative to dairy milk.

Nuts and seeds

You may not think of eating these very often, but nuts and seeds are a highly nutritious and natural food for humans. As well as protein they provide healthy fat and a range of vitamins and minerals, especially zinc, calcium and magnesium. Almonds, cashews and peanuts are highest in protein (they consist of about 20 per cent protein, which is comparable to fish, poultry and meat), followed by Brazil nuts, hazelnuts, pine nuts and walnuts.

Fresh raw nuts and seeds are the best option. Roasted and salted nuts have usually been processed at a high temperature, so the fat they contain is not so healthy – and they often contain excess salt. Nuts and seeds make great snacks, on their own or with fruit or yogurt. Add them to salads or breakfast cereals or bake them in bread. And don't forget peanut butter; many shops now also sell cashew, almond and other nut butters. Look for brands that don't have any added sugar and salt.

Soya beans

These have the highest protein content of any beans – hence their inclusion here rather than with pulses in the 'low-glycaemic carbohydrates' section. Soya beans and soya protein products such as tofu

contain isoflavones, substances that appear to lower LDL cholesterol. They also protect against oxidation, a process many believe to be more implicated in heart disease than the level of LDL cholesterol.

Soya beans are not readily available unless you live near an Oriental market. However, you can sometimes find them (often under the name of edamame, which are young soya beans, usually still in their pods) in restaurants that serve Asian-style food. Products made from soya beans are easier to find: try tofu, tempeh and soya milk rather than any of the more highly processed 'mock meat' foods.

Protein-rich pasta and bars

You can now buy protein-rich dry pasta with as much as 50 per cent protein (regular pasta has around 10 per cent). Pasta with a very high proportion of protein has a rubbery texture, but some brands that contain 25–30 per cent protein can taste almost identical to regular pasta. It is usually enriched with soya protein and it has a lower GL than regular pasta, so it is especially suitable for people who are overweight or have diabetes.

Protein bars are becoming more readily available and can be a useful standby for people who don't have time to put together a protein-rich snack or small meal. The best of these are rather expensive because they contain the same amount of protein as one chicken breast, a wide range of vitamins and minerals and very little carbohydrate and fat. They are not meant to be eaten every day.

Low-glycaemic carbohydrates

These make up the B part of your plate, as described on page 21. Low-glycaemic carbohydrates are mainly vegetables, pulses (which are also a good source of protein) and low-GL fruit (some fruits have a medium GL).

As you are by now aware, the carbohydrates in food stimulate the secretion of insulin to varying degrees. The Greek Doctor's Diet is designed to keep the production of insulin low, thus keeping blood sugar stable. The result is a lower average insulin level and increased fat burning. This is not achieved by cutting out carbohydrates – which is not good for health – but by ensuring that the majority of the carbohydrates you eat are low-glycaemic carbs that raise blood sugar slowly and thus do not over-stimulate insulin secretion.

As a rule of thumb, the less physically active, the more overweight or insulin-resistant you are, the less carbohydrate you should eat. That said, it is difficult to get too much carbohydrate from eating vegetables, pulses and low-GL fruit. However, it is all too easy when you eat sugar and other high-GL foods such as bread, potatoes, pasta, rice and flour products. If you are overweight, you need to eat less sugar and starch, and more vegetables and pulses.

Vegetables

Vegetables are crucial to good health and an aid to weight reduction. Because of the soluble fibre in vegetables, the carbohydrates are absorbed slowly, providing a gradual conversion to blood sugar. This results in a lower and more stable insulin level in the blood. The non-soluble fibre in vegetables increase the volume of the food and the feeling of satiety. This combination of soluble and non-soluble fibre gives you blood sugar control and reduces the feeling of hunger.

There is, however, a lot more to vegetables than fibre. They are also packed with antioxidants and phytochemicals that protect against various diseases. For example, dark green vegetables and brightly coloured vegetables such as broccoli, cabbage, Brussels sprouts, peppers (capsicums) and tomatoes protect against cancer, while the onion group (garlic, onion, spring onion, leek, chives) offers similar protection and can help lower cholesterol and blood pressure.

Your best insurance against disease is a refrigerator filled with fresh vegetables, but don't forget frozen ones also have their place. They are a valuable source of nutrients and in fact often retain more vitamins than their fresh counterparts. Some canned vegetables are also useful: no kitchen should be without canned tomatoes, while more unusual canned vegetables such as artichoke hearts are convenient and taste great cooked with a little olive oil and lemon juice.

Take care when cooking vegetables. Boiling is not the best way to prepare them because so many water-soluble vitamins and trace minerals are discarded along with the water. Steaming is a much better method. You should also eat salads and raw vegetables as often as possible.

Pulses

Beans, lentils and chickpeas are a valuable addition to any diet: they are certainly not just for vegetarians. Once you have decided to reduce your intake of potatoes, rice and pasta dramatically, pulses will become very important to you. They are low-glycaemic and contain a lot of protein, fibre, vitamins, minerals and healthy fatty acids. If you want more stable blood sugar and lower insulin production, the answer is simple: get to know your beans and pulses!

They have been proven to lower the level of LDL cholesterol and triglycerides in the blood and to increase the 'good' HDL cholesterol. They protect against cancer and are rich in calcium and iron. They are also the best source of soluble fibre in food; this type of fibre increases the feeling of satiety and gives good blood sugar control. Once called 'poor people's meat', pulses also have the added advantage of being great value.

There are numerous types of beans and lentils to choose from, both dried and canned. Beans that you have soaked and cooked yourself do have a lower GI than canned beans, but the difference is not significant; both types are perfectly acceptable. If you do soak your own beans, it is a good idea to cook a large portion, as they will keep for days in the refrigerator and also freeze well. Dried lentils do not need to be soaked but they do need to be boiled for 20 to 30 minutes.

Fruit

Most types of fruit have a low glycaemic effect, partly because of their high fibre content and partly because the natural sweetness of fruit comes from fructose. Fructose, or fruit sugar, has a very low GI, 19 – far lower than sucrose (table sugar), with a GI of 68. Cherries and grapefruit have a particularly low GI; plums, peaches, pears, apples, oranges, grapes, strawberries and other berries also have a low GI. Bananas and some tropical fruits have somewhat higher glycaemic effect, so don't eat these too regularly.

You should eat more vegetables than fruit, but fruit is nonetheless very important to a balanced diet. As well as fibre, fruit is an excellent source of vitamins, minerals and other antioxidants. Oranges contain a lot of potassium, folic acid and vitamin C. Strawberries, raspberries and kiwi fruit are even richer sources of vitamin C, while figs are a source of calcium. Several phytochemicals in fruit can also help protect against cancer.

Most people like the taste of fruit, and fresh fruit can satisfy your craving for something sweet without giving you a lot of fat or starch at the same time. A combination of yogurt, fruit and nuts is a healthy between-meals snack.

Medium- and high-glycaemic carbohydrates

These are the foods that form the C part of the ABC reward meal. By this, I mean that they should be eaten in moderation, when for many people, particularly those who are overweight, these foods are a central part of their diet.

Fibre

Although dietary fibre (an indigestible form of carbohydrate) contributes little energy, it plays a very important role in human health. Almost all the fibre that we get from our diet comes from vegetables, fruit, pulses, grains and nuts. There are two main types of fibre: soluble and insoluble. Soluble fibre ensures the proper digestion of nutrients, and means the bowels absorb carbohydrates more slowly, thus blood sugar rises at a steadier level over a longer period of time. Soluble fibre also lowers cholesterol and is prebiotic, i.e. it supports good intestinal health. Soluble fibre is found in beans and lentils, oats, vegetables and fruit. Non-soluble dietary fibre, which is found mainly in whole grains, increases the volume of food and aids bowel function. It is believed that the fibre in our diet can prevent some forms of cancer, such as colon cancer, but this might also be due to other substances in fruit and vegetables.

Most people in the Western world consume much less than 20 g of fibre per day. The official recommendation is 30 g daily. An easy way to increase your intake of dietary fibre is to eat two fruits and at least three to four servings of vegetables a day. Eating lentils and beans instead of potatoes and bread, for example, will also increase the amount of fibre in your diet. When you increase the amount of fibre in your diet, you should also increase your water intake, to ensure regular bowel function.

Bread

Bread is a very important part of food culture. Too important, one could argue, because it is often eaten as part of every meal. How healthy is bread for you? Well, we really do not need grain products at all to live a healthy and long life, but whole grains do contain protein, fibre, vitamins and minerals. In that respect they contribute in a positive way to our diet, as long as they do not dominate and replace other foods. However, that is exactly what is happening today. Grain products such as refined wheat flour, bread, pasta, cakes, biscuits and cereals make up a substantial part of what we eat every day. These products contain a lot of energy and carbohydrates. They also tend to be made from highly refined flour, with little in the way of fibre, protein, vitamins and minerals.

Ideally, we should not eat bread or grains at all, but it would be naive to think that we could cease doing it. Besides, bread and other baked products taste good. Instead we should regard bread as something that should be eaten in restricted amounts – and chosen with care.

Bread and flour products vary significantly in their glycaemic effect, depending on the flour they are made of. The finer the flour, the quicker blood sugar and insulin will rise after consumption. The GL of bread per 100 g varies between 30 and 50. Unfortunately, most of the bread that is sold is highly refined and contains more than 80 per cent fine wheat flour, which gives you a lot of energy, but little nourishment.

When buying bread do not be fooled by products described as 'brown' or 'multi-grain' bread. They generally contain mostly fine wheat flour because it is the cheapest raw material there is. The colour of a bread does not necessarily indicate that it is a wholegrain product – if you use sufficient colour (malt), you could make fine bread that is almost black. And a bread that is 'multi-grain' need not contain any 'whole' grains at all.

Sweet but dangerous

Is there room for sweet things in a healthy diet? Of course there is. However, the source of sweetness you choose is very important. Sugars are part of the cellular structure of many foods such as whole fruit and vegetables. It is not these, but the vast amount of so-called added sugars – those found in honey, table sugar (and other sugars such as demerara, cane sugar, muscovado), fruit juices, baked goods, confectionery, convenience foods and so on – that are causing so many of today's health problems. If you wish to lose weight or gain control of your blood sugar levels, wherever possible you should avoid products that contain sucrose, or table sugar; glucose, glucose syrup or corn syrup (these concentrated syrups are widely used by the food industry); honey (which contains glucose, fructose and sucrose); and maltose, the sugar that is found in beer. As a rule of thumb, no more than 10 per cent of your daily energy intake should come from added sugars. With an intake of 2000 calories, that would mean a maximum of 50 g (1¾ oz) of added sugar a day. The average daily intake of added sugars in the western world is far greater than this.

As you may know, the sugar contained in fruit is fructose. Fructose reacts differently in the body from other kinds of sugar. It is absorbed more slowly in the small intestine and cannot be converted into energy immediately. Fructose has a very small effect on blood sugar, and a low GI of 19 (the GI of sucrose is 68). I recommend that, wherever possible, you should substitute fructose or no-cal sweeteners for other sugars, but also that you reduce your consumption of sugar in all forms. Fructose and artificial sweeteners are not a necessary part of any diet, they are just a better alternative to sugar. Fruit is also not recommended in unlimited quantities; in particular limit your intake of medium-glycaemic fruits, such as bananas. In general I recommend no more than two pieces of fruit a day.

What matters is how coarse and heavy the bread is. Whole grains weigh more than fine flour, and this is how you can assess how coarse a loaf of bread is. The coarser the bread, the lower the GL.

The type of grain is also important. Rye and barley give a lower GL than wheat. However, if you prefer wheat breads look for a heavy loaf that is labelled 'stoneground wholemeal'. Alternatively, you may be able to find bread made from spelt. Spelt is an ancient type of wheat that has become increasingly popular in recent years. It has roughly the same GL as wholemeal wheat, i.e. relatively high, but it contains a bit more protein, more fibre and more vitamins and minerals. It also seems to be tolerated better by those with poor tolerance to regular wheat.

Nuts and seeds such as sunflower, pumpkin and flax will also reduce the GL of bread and add more protein, healthy fat and fibre. Sourdough bread has a slightly lower GL than other breads, because acidity reduces the glycaemic effect of foods.

Coarse bread is more expensive than bread made from highly refined flour, but remember that you pay a lot for air when you buy baguettes. Keep in mind though that even the coarsest bread will range from medium to high GL – it is never low GL.

Pasta

Many people are surprised to learn that pasta has a lower GI than bread. That is because pasta is normally made from durum wheat (semolina), which has a lower GI than regular wheat. Durum wheat flour is coarser and contains somewhat more protein. Also, the less you cook the pasta, the lower its GL. Pasta cooked until it is 'al dente', which gives you something to chew on, is better for the blood sugar than pasta that has been cooked for longer.

Rather than choosing white pasta, opt for one made from wholemeal durum wheat, as it contains more fibre, vitamins and minerals than the more refined variety. It was once only available in health food shops but most supermarkets now sell it in the form of either fusilli or spaghetti. And don't forget the protein-enriched pasta discussed on page 39 – it's a very good choice.

Pasta can also be made by using a proportion of other types of grain, such as barley, flour from white lentils, mung beans and soya beans, which gives a much lower GL. On the other hand, gluten-free pasta is normally made from corn, millet or buckwheat, which gives it a higher GL. Always bear in mind that serving size is vital – many people eat pasta in over-large portions.

Rice

There is a wide – and confusing – array of rice varieties, but which of them is best for your blood sugar? Rice can vary from medium to high GI, depending on type and how it is cooked. Short-grained, sticky Asian (jasmine and sushi) rice has a high GL and should be avoided. Long-grain basmati rice is a better choice. 'Parboiled' long-grain American rice also has a lower GL, as it is steamed before being processed further, which makes the rice less sticky and gives it a lower GL. As a rule of thumb: the stickier the rice is after it has been cooked, the higher the GL. Brown rice does not have a significantly lower GL than parboiled white rice but it does contain more of the shell and is richer in fibre, vitamins and minerals, so it is the healthiest choice. Wild rice, which is not a rice but a type of grass, is another good choice as it has a low GL, lots of fibre and a pleasant nutty taste.

Other grains

Oats Old-fashioned rolled oats (the ones with the big flakes) have a lower GL than the pre-cooked variety, so these are the better choice. You can use oats to make porridge of course, but oatmeal can also replace some of the wheat flour in many recipes, such as muffins, bread, pancakes, biscuits, pie pastry and pizzas.

Barley Barley has a pleasantly nutty taste and a lower GL than many other grains. It is therefore an excellent alternative to rice and potatoes, as a side dish or in soups and stews – why not try 'barleyotto' instead of 'risotto'? You can also use it when you bake, but bear in mind that barley contains very little gluten so if you want bread that leavens and is elastic, you need to add 10 g gluten flour per 100 g barley flour.

Buckwheat Roasted buckwheat kernels (also called 'kasha') have a medium GL and are a good alternative to rice in cereals and porridge.

Bulgur and couscous Bulgur is coarsely chopped durum wheat that has been partially pre-cooked and dried; couscous is simply a finer variety of bulgur. Both grains take just a few minutes to prepare and are a good choice of grain, having a relatively low GL.

Quinoa Called the 'mother grain' by the Incas, quinoa is high in protein and has a relatively low GL. It has a slightly nutty flavour and is a good alternative to rice in savoury dishes. It is widely available in health food shops and some of the larger supermarkets.

Breakfast cereals

Breakfast cereals are easy and convenient; many people eat them every day. This is not something I recommend but if you are one of those people it is important to find a cereal that is minimally processed and unsweetened. This can be tricky, as most cereals are high-glycaemic and prepared from highly processed grains. Corn flakes, for example, have a very high GL. Did you know that a 30 g (1 oz) serving of corn flakes gives you a similar increase in blood sugar and insulin to an equal amount of pure sugar?

Opt for cereals that are high in fibre – All-Bran is a good example – and have no added sugar. Don't assume that because something has a 'healthy' reputation it will be suitable for a low-glycaemic

lifestyle – muesli is often sweetened and most brands contain dried fruit, which has a high GL. A much better alternative is unsweetened muesli made from grains and seeds, and with a minimal amount of dried fruit (preferably none at all).

Whichever cereal you choose, if you add milk and berries, chopped nuts, ground flaxseeds or soya flakes, or a spoonful of yogurt, this will lower its GL. And if you must sweeten your cereal, use a little fructose – not sugar.

Potatoes

Many people find it strange that potatoes have a high GI – after all, they are a vegetable aren't they? Yes they are but the human body lacks the enzymes to digest raw potato and it must be cooked. Cooking potato alters its starch content, making it more easily digestible. Cooked potato causes a rapid rise in blood sugar and insulin levels. It is worth bearing in mind that potatoes, along with grain, are one of the most efficient foods for fattening domestic animals.

By all means, have potatoes once in a while as the C part of your reward meal, at least if you are happy with your weight. But steer clear of crisps and chips. They have been fried in plant oils and can contain harmful by-products from heated oil.

Fats and oils

Fat – the right kind of course – is a vital part of the Greek Doctor's Diet. In the 'Food, health and weight' section I looked at why good fats are so important in achieving good health; the following guidance will help you translate that information into good choices at the supermarket.

Choosing fats and oils

Monounsaturated fat This should be the type of fat you eat most of, as monounsaturated fat increases good (HDL) cholesterol levels and helps keep down bad (LDL) cholesterol. Almonds, avocados, Brazil nuts, cashew nuts, hazelnuts, macadamia nuts, olives, peanuts, pecan nuts and pistachio nuts are very rich in monounsaturated fat. The healthiest types of oils are extra virgin olive oil, and cold-pressed rapeseed (canola) oil and avocado oil, as these contain mainly monounsaturated fat.

Omega-3, polyunsaturated fat Most of us get too little omega-3 fatty acids and should increase our intake. Omega-3s have many benefits; in particular they have a protective effect against cardiovascular disease and because they are an essential component of the brain, they are thought to lift depression and even improve intelligence. The best source is oily fish such as salmon, sardines, mackerel, herring and tuna, as well as cod liver oil (as a supplement). Flaxseed is the richest source of omega-3 in the plant world, with as much as 58 per cent health-friendly omega-3 fatty acids. Adding a tablespoon of cold-pressed flaxseed oil to food just before you eat it will boost your omega-3 intake.

Omega-6, polyunsaturated fat Though essential, omega-6 fatty acids are consumed in far greater quantities than necessary in the modern world. Corn, sunflower, safflower and soya bean oils, and the margarines derived from them, are all high in omega-6s and are widely used both in home cooking and by the food industry. To reduce your intake, switch from using sunflower, corn, soya and other refined oils and margarines to cold-pressed or extra-virgin oils – mainly olive oil – and avoid eating fried foods too frequently.

Saturated fat Many people eat far more saturated fat than they need, in the form of saturated fats from full-fat dairy products (milk, butter, cream and cheese), meat, cakes, biscuits and pastries. Saturated fat is non-essential and thus not desirable in large quantities as it displaces the healthier and essential unsaturated fat. Moderate amounts of saturated fat will not do you any harm; it is when saturated fats are eaten to excess, as part of a high-glycaemic diet, that problems arise.

Trans fats These man-made fats, also known as hydrogenated (or partially hydrogenated) vegetable oils and fats, should be avoided wherever possible. Trans fatty acids are associated with a greatly increased risk of heart disease and many other inflammatory and degenerative diseases. They are found in many margarines, vegetable shortenings and yellow fat spreads, and are widely used in the food industry to increase the shelf life of foods. The majority of ready-made foods contain significant amounts of trans fats so always check the labels and avoid foods that list 'partially hydrogenated (vegetable) fat' among the ingredients.

In the kitchen

I grew up in Greece, in a family that really knew how to appreciate good food. My grandmother in particular was a good cook. I cannot remember that she ever used a recipe or consulted a cookery book, yet much of what I know about cooking is thanks to her. I was allowed to be an apprentice in her kitchen, which is why today I am able to cook and create new recipes without using cookbooks. Unlike my grandmother, however, I have a considerable collection of cookbooks from around the world. I refer to them often, both for information and inspiration. But I rarely use the recipes, at least not by the book. I have arrived at this set of rules:

▶ Never trust a recipe 100 per cent (ovens vary and the quality of ingredients vary, so always use your common sense).
▶ Never read a cookery book when you are hungry, but preferably after a meal or at night.
▶ Never try out a new recipe on your guests.

My grandmother's cooking was excellent, but the menu was relatively simple and traditional; it made full use of Greece's wide range of home-grown ingredients, in particular vegetables, fruit, pulses and nuts. If you want to cook healthy, interesting food it is important to find out as much as you can about the ingredients that are available to you, and learn how to use them. Sadly, despite the fact that we have so many cookery books and magazines that feature delicious recipes, it seems that many people feel that preparing a home-cooked meal is too much trouble, and they end up eating frozen pizza or a takeaway for dinner. To cook 'from scratch' often means heating up a pasta sauce.

We have discovered exciting food from other cultures, but find it difficult to prepare this food ourselves. We have so many demands on our time – work, household chores, hobbies and keeping up with friends – that we are always busy. When you get home from work, you have perhaps not given much thought to what you and the rest of the family should eat. You open the refrigerator and take a look inside. You see many different ingredients, but nothing that is suitable for dinner. If you start reading recipes, you find that you lack one or more ingredients. So it's frozen pizza again… This is why – even if you love trying new recipes – it is important to learn to cook without a cookbook.

Planning is important if you want to eat well. If you do not plan ahead, it is even more important that you are able to cook with the ingredients you have to hand. This becomes much easier if you have a well-stocked larder and have familiarized yourself with a few cooking techniques and basic recipes. Liberate yourself from cookery books, at least during the week, and start with the ingredients you have at home or can buy easily. You will be surprised to learn how simple and exciting it is to cook without recipes.

Kitchen equipment

If you are serious about cooking healthily, it is important to make sure that you have the appropriate utensils. In addition to good-quality pots and pans, knives and so on, I recommend a food processor, a hand-held electric blender and a core temperature/meat thermometer: these are particularly useful for preparing simple healthy food. An ice cream machine is admittedly not a necessity, but I recommend it if you want to make delicious ice cream that isn't full of additives and doesn't cost a fortune. The choice of kitchen equipment is, to a certain extent, personal but most of the items in the following list are kitchen essentials and will help you prepare the recipes in this book.

chef's knife with 20 cm (8 in) blade
paring knife with 5 cm (2 in) blade
filleting knife
serrated knife
carving knife
carving fork
knife sharpener
non-stick saucepans (large,
    medium and small)
large non-stick frying pan, with lid
small non-stick frying pan (can
    also be used as an
    omelette pan)
non-stick wok
casserole (enamelled cast
    iron is good)
roasting tins, large and small
ridged chargrill pan
vegetable steamer
chopping boards (one for raw
    meat and fish, one for
    vegetables)
wooden spoons

slotted spoon
fish slice
tongs
poultry shears
vegetable peeler
metal skewers
ladle
balloon whisk
cheese grater
zest grater
lemon squeezer
garlic press
pitter (for olives)
apple corer
can opener
measuring jug
measuring spoons
pestle and mortar
pepper mill
salt mill
kitchen scales
kitchen timer
kitchen scissors

mixing bowls
large stainless steel bowl
rubber spatula
baking tray
23 cm (9 in) cake tin
loaf tin
ramekins
large colander
strainer
fine sieve
screwtop jar
airtight containers for
    storing food
disposable rubber gloves (for
    chopping chillies)
pastry brush
nailbrush (for cleaning mussels)
tweezers (for fish bones)
food processor with
    dough hook
hand-held blender
core temperature thermometer
ice cream machine

Stocking your pantry, refrigerator and freezer

A well-stocked kitchen makes it easy to prepare meals with minimum fuss and last-minute shopping. You are also more likely to experiment with exciting new recipes if you have most of the ingredients to hand. I keep a list of items I have run out of, so I can stock up next time I go shopping.

Remember that some items have a limited shelf life, so turn out your kitchen cupboards every two or three months. Nuts – including peanut butter – and seeds quickly become rancid, while dried herbs and spices lose their individual aromas. The following are suggestions for your shopping list.

Kitchen cupboards

sodium-reduced salt

whole peppercorns, ground white pepper

oils: extra virgin olive oil, cold-pressed rapeseed (canola) oil, cold-pressed avocado oil, cold-pressed walnut oil, sesame oil

clarified butter (ghee): it keeps for months and tolerates high temperatures without burning

vinegars: white wine, red wine, balsamic, raspberry, cider, rice

sauces: soy sauce, Tabasco, Worcestershire sauce, mayonnaise, sweet chilli sauce, Chinese oyster sauce, Thai fish sauce, Indonesian ketjap mani

mustard: wholegrain, Dijon, tarragon

pesto

spices: allspice, aniseed, caraway seeds, cardamom, cayenne pepper, chilli powder, whole and ground cinnamon, cloves, ground coriander, cumin, curry, fennel seeds, ginger, whole and ground nutmeg, turmeric, saffron

vanilla pods and vanilla extract

dried herbs: bay leaves, oregano, thyme, rosemary, marjoram, sage, tarragon, mint

reduced-sodium stock, ready-made concentrated stock or vegetable bouillon powder

canned coconut milk

canned tomatoes

black and green olives

canned artichoke hearts

canned beans, chickpeas and lentils

dried lentils: red, brown, green

jars of hummus and tahini (sesame seed paste)

canned fish: anchovies, mackerel, sardines, tuna

nuts: whole and ground almonds, Brazil nuts, peanuts, pine nuts, pistachios, cashews, walnuts, pecans, macadamia nuts

unsweetened peanut butter

seeds: sunflower, flax, pumpkin, sesame

dried apricots

chocolate (at least 70% cocoa solids, or sugar-free)

onions

garlic

porridge oats

couscous

quinoa

various flakes (rye, spelt, oatmeal)

buckwheat

pearl barley

pasta: wholewheat spaghetti or fusilli, or protein-enriched pasta

rice: brown basmati, American long-grain parboiled rice, wild

flour: stoneground wholemeal, spelt, barley, soya, chickpea (gram), rye, durum wheat (fine semolina)

thickeners: cornflour, arrowroot

baking powder

dried yeast

fructose (fruit sugar)

white and red wine, port, sherry

Fruit bowl

lemons, limes

apples

berries (raspberries, blueberries, strawberries etc.)

pears

oranges, tangerines

peaches, nectarines

apricots

cherries

melon, watermelon

plums

grapefruit

kiwi fruit

grapes

pomegranate

passion fruit

Refrigerator

eggs

cold-pressed flaxseed oil

skimmed milk or soya milk

double cream, single cream, soya cream with 18% and 36% fat

crème fraîche, sour cream (reduced fat if available)

yogurt: low-fat natural, or fat-free fruit yogurt with fructose, or soya yogurt

cottage cheese, ricotta, fromage frais, quark

cheese: feta, Parmesan, mature Cheddar, Gruyère

mustard

tomato purée (paste)

curry paste

olives and olive paste

anchovy paste

horseradish

ginger

chilli

fresh herbs: basil, mint, thyme, parsley

vegetables such as aubergine (eggplant), carrots, celery, courgette (zucchini), cucumber, red and green peppers (capsicums), tomatoes, fennel, cabbage, broccoli, Brussels sprouts, cauliflower, salad leaves (e.g. lettuce, chicory, rocket, watercress), leeks, spring onions, mushrooms, spinach, asparagus, bean sprouts, green beans, onions, pak choi (bok choy), radishes

In the freezer

If your freezer contains meat, fish and vegetables, you will always have the basis for a good healthy meal in the house.

spinach

peas

broad beans

broccoli florets

berries: blackberries, blueberries, raspberries, blackcurrants, redcurrants, cranberries

shellfish: prawns, scampi, squid (not breaded or battered)

fish: fillets of salmon, cod, haddock, turbot, plaice

chicken breasts and legs, skinless and boneless

whole chicken

turkey breasts

turkey or chicken, minced

duck breasts

meat: beef fillet, stewing beef, lean minced beef

lamb: leg of lamb, fillet, lean minced lamb

pork: fillet/tenderloin

homemade or other coarse wholegrain bread, sliced

Spice it up

You can make food more interesting by adding one or two fresh or dried herbs, spices or other taste enhancers. Below I've suggested some classic pairings, and some more unusual combinations that work surprisingly well. If you want to give something a Chinese flavour, use ginger and spring onions and finish with a few drops of soy sauce and sesame oil. For a South-east Asian touch, include garlic and chilli, plus lime juice and Asian fish sauce. As well as making food taste great, herbs and spices contain a myriad of important bioactive ingredients. So don't let your herbs and spices gather dust in the cupboard – use them every day.

With fish Fennel, dill, parsley, tarragon, chives, coriander, thyme, oregano, turmeric, mustard, curry, vinegar, lemon, lime, white wine

With shellfish Basil, parsley, dill, marjoram, chives, curry, coriander, tarragon, oregano, thyme, chilli, garlic, lemon, lime, mustard, coconut milk, white wine, sherry

With poultry Basil, oregano, garlic, chives, curry, tarragon, bay leaves, ginger, cinnamon, marjoram, thyme, chilli, turmeric, vinegar, lemon, lime, orange, mustard, coconut milk, red wine, white wine, sherry

With beef Garlic, cumin, allspice, oregano, thyme, marjoram, curry, basil, cayenne, chilli, bay leaves, mustard, horseradish, red wine, port

With lamb Garlic, oregano, basil, dill, rosemary, thyme, mint, allspice, cumin, red wine

With pork Garlic, dill, coriander, cumin, rosemary, thyme, cayenne, allspice, sage, ginger, lemon, curry, mustard, sherry, red and white wine

With game Garlic, juniper berries, thyme, oregano, bay leaves, allspice, rosemary, red wine, port

With eggs Tarragon, chives, cayenne, basil, curry

With dried beans and lentils Garlic, parsley, chives, coriander, cumin, curry, tarragon, marjoram, rosemary, thyme, sage, chilli, cayenne, lemon

With asparagus Basil, dill, tarragon, chives, nutmeg

With peas Mint, basil, tarragon, chives, oregano, dill, marjoram, thyme

With broccoli, cauliflower, Brussels sprouts, cabbage Garlic, cumin, basil, tarragon, curry, marjoram, ginger, oregano, thyme

With spinach Garlic, nutmeg, dill, chives, basil, tarragon, coconut milk, chilli

With aubergine (eggplant) Garlic, parsley, chilli, oregano, marjoram, basil, mint, sage, thyme

With courgettes (zucchini) Garlic, parsley, oregano, dill, chives, tarragon, marjoram, basil, mint, sage, thyme

With green beans Parsley, basil, garlic, tarragon, dill, marjoram, rosemary

With mushrooms Garlic, parsley, oregano, marjoram, basil, chives, dill, tarragon

With peppers (capsicums) Garlic, coriander, chives, oregano, thyme, marjoram

With tomatoes Garlic, chives, coriander, tarragon, oregano, marjoram, thyme, sage, chilli, cayenne, mustard, cumin

Planning to eat well

You should always plan your meals. You plan the agenda for a meeting or nothing would get done; you plan to have clean clothes to put on in the morning; why should food be an exception? Planning ahead saves time and money, and makes it easier to eat healthily. If you wait until you're hungry before you buy food, you're likely to end up with an expensive ready-made meal or takeaway, packed with unhealthy fats and lacking in vitamins and minerals.

Making a weekly plan means that you can do most of your food shopping on one day, rather than trailing round the shops after work when you're tired and hungry. Also, by planning what you are going to eat in this way, you will waste far less food. A staggering amount of food is thrown away because it has languished in the refrigerator for too long. However, planning doesn't mean you can't be flexible: for example, if you see some lovely fresh broad beans at the market, you can easily swop them for the vegetables on your plan.

I've suggested a couple of weekly menu plans on pages 26–29; you can use these as inspiration for your own plans, but just remember that you must always include a variety of foods so you get a good range of essential vitamins and minerals.

Putting together a list of meals for the coming week also means you can do a lot of advance preparation. Why not prepare tomorrow's meals after you have had your dinner and relaxed for a while? That way, you avoid having to cook when you come home tired and hungry. If nearly everything is ready in advance, all you will need to do is to heat up the food.

Preparing larger amounts of food and having them later in the week is also a good idea. Why not set aside two or three hours at the weekend to cook casseroles, baked dishes, beans and lentils? Or double the quantities of a recipe, then divide it into portions and store in the refrigerator or freezer. That way, you will not have to prepare meals from scratch every night of the week.

Make ahead

 Many of the recipes in this book can be prepared ahead of time or in larger quantities. These recipes are marked with this symbol, and give advice on storage times. I've also included lots of tips on variations, so you won't feel as though you're eating the same meal two days in a row.

Preparing larger amounts of food makes good sense. Have you ever thought how professional chefs manage to cook so many different dishes in one day? By preparing a variety of stocks, sauces and garnishes and by doing as much advance preparation as possible, it becomes comparatively simple to put ingredients together in different combinations. This can save you both time and money. For example:

▶ From a basic minced meat sauce you can easily prepare 4 or 5 different meals (serve it with spaghetti; with tomato, avocado and fajitas; or as as the basis for moussaka or lasagne).

▶ Lentil and bean dishes are particularly good when cooked in advance. Reheat them and add herbs, spices, sauces or other ingredients, such as grilled bacon, halved cherry tomatoes or cubes of cheese.

▶ As well as preparing whole dishes in advance, also think about the various parts of a meal that could be used for other purposes: for example, the almond and garlic sauce on page 104 is delicious served with fish or as a dip so it's a good idea to make extra. This principle can be applied to many other sauces.

Basic cooking techniques

Making stock

The basis of so much cooking is a good stock, and it is quite simple to prepare. Butchers and fishmongers will often give you bones for free.

For a meat or chicken stock, roast the bones in the oven, together with carrot, onion, celery and leeks, until the bones are well browned. Transfer everything to a large saucepan, cover with water, bring to the boil and simmer (skimming the surface often) on a low heat for 1 to 6 hours, depending on how strongly flavoured you want the stock. When the stock is ready, strain it into a clean saucepan and boil it to concentrate the flavour further. You can also boil it down to a syrupy consistency, which will give you a concentrated stock that can be used as a basis for sauces and soups.

To make fish stock, combine the shells of 450 g (1 lb) prawns, 225g (8 oz) firm-fleshed fish, 1 chopped celery stick, 1 thickly sliced small onion, 1 bay leaf, a squeeze of lemon juice and 6 whole peppercorns in a saucepan and cover with 1.2 litres (2 pints) of water. Bring to boiling point, then reduce the heat to low, cover, and simmer gently for 20 minutes, or until the fish falls apart. Strain carefully to remove any bones.

You will find a recipe for vegetable stock in the recipe for Greek vegetable soup on page 59. Alternatively, use organic bouillon powder.

Store stock in the refrigerator for 2 to 3 days (2 days for fish stock) or freeze it. Concentrated stock can be frozen in ice cube trays.

Slow-roasting

Flavours develop in a fantastic way at low temperatures, and the food will be so tender and succulent that you will not need extra salt or rich sauces. However, cooking at low temperatures takes longer than at high temperatures, and this has to be taken into consideration before you begin.

Preheat the oven to its lowest setting – usually about 120°C/250°F/gas ½. Put a roasting tin over a low heat, add a few of teaspoons of olive oil, plus herbs, garlic, mustard or other flavourings, and then place the meat, poultry or fish in the pan and insert a meat thermometer into the thickest part. Remove from the oven when the core temperature has been reached: 55–65°C is fine for most meats that should be pink inside, whereas chicken and turkey should be 65–70°C.

The fricassée principle

This means that you cook meat, poultry or fish together with vegetables in stock until everything is tender. To complete the dish, strain the stock, thicken it and add your chosen seasonings, herbs and spices. You can thicken the stock with cornflour dissolved in a little cold water, or with egg yolks. If you use egg yolks, mix them with a few spoonfuls of the hot stock, then add them to the pot and stir well. Do not let it boil, or the egg yolks will curdle. You can also use single cream or soya cream, or a mixture of egg yolk, cream and thickener.

Alternatively, for a healthy thickener, add well-mashed or puréed red or yellow lentils or high-fibre vegetables, such as celery, tomatoes and/or onion. Serve the fricassée with mashed or puréed peas, beans or lentils, or with pasta or rice if it is your reward meal.

Ragouts and casseroles

There is not much difference between a ragout and a fricassée. The main difference is that when you make a ragout, you brown the ingredients first and often add tomatoes in one form or another (chopped tomatoes or tomato purée/paste). Apart from that you follow the procedure for fricassée, but you do not need to strain the stock. Wine and more powerful spices and herbs such as chilli, mustard, allspice and caraway seeds are often used in ragouts. Tougher cuts of meat such as shank and neck benefit from the long, slow cooking process, but the result is just as good – and cooking times shorter – with poultry, better pieces of meat, vegetables and fish.

Stir-frying

This cooking method originated in the Far East, but has now become very popular worldwide. It is a very good way of preparing healthy food, because it is quick and uses only a small amount of oil. The best oils for stir-frying are extra virgin olive oil or sesame oil, which are rich in monounsaturated fat and tolerate quick heating better than oils with a high proportion of polyunsaturated fat, such as sunflower oil, soya oil or corn oil. As the cooking time is so quick, you should always choose

Frying is bad news

Frying and deep frying are two of the most popular cooking methods. Unfortunately, they are also the most harmful cooking methods. The health hazard is a result of quick oxidation and other chemical changes that take place when oils are exposed to high temperatures, light and air. The chemicals these reactions produce are downright toxic. If you only use oil for frying very occasionally, your body can handle the toxins. Used every week – or even every day, as many people do – these waste substances accumulate in our cells and can trigger illnesses such as heart disease or cancer.

Should we then just stop frying and deep frying completely? Ideally, yes, though few of us are likely to do this. Therefore it is useful to know which fats are the least harmful for frying and deep frying. Polyunsaturated fat does not tolerate high temperatures well. Fish fat and the fat in most vegetable oils is polyunsaturated and is not suitable for frying. Consequently, you should avoid frying fatty fish. Monounsaturated and saturated fats tolerate high temperatures better. Olive oil and sesame oil mainly contain monounsaturated fat, and tolerate frying at low temperatures relatively well, but not deep frying. If you must fry at high temperatures or deep-fry, clarified butter (ghee) and unrefined coconut oil are preferable (although they contain a lot of saturated fat, they are stable at high temperatures and produce fewer harmful substances).

Avoid frying with lard, which consists almost wholly of saturated fat. Also avoid using cheaper margarines and hydrogenated oils. These are often totally artificial products, and are likely to contain trans fatty acids.

If you wish to fry food, stir-frying is your best option, because the fat and the food are only exposed to high temperatures for a short time. Another alternative is to cook your ingredients in a little stock or boiling water, and then fry them for a very short time at a low temperature.

tender cuts of meat (preferably fillet), fish or poultry for the wok.

First you need to chop or slice all your ingredients and have them ready by the wok. Heat the wok to a high temperature, add a little oil, then add your main ingredient and stir over the heat until it begins to colour (chicken and other poultry should be well done); remove from the pan. Now add the vegetables, stirring all the time. You should fry tough vegetables such as broccoli, cauliflower, onion and peppers (capsicums) first, and then add more tender vegetables, such as spring onion, asparagus and mangetouts. Put the main ingredient back in the pan and season to taste. Soy sauce, ginger, chilli, sesame oil and garlic are commonly used ingredients, but you can also give the food a Mediterranean touch by using garlic, pesto, oregano, thyme and tarragon or an Indonesian touch by adding peanut butter and coconut milk. You can also use the wok to prepare desserts based on fruits and berries.

Meatballs and fishcakes

Lean meat, game and poultry, fish and shellfish, minced or very finely chopped, make a good, simple supper dish. Quality and freshness are very important, so don't just focus on price. If you buy ready-minced meat, make sure it's not full of fat or ice/water. Add herbs or spices, finely chopped onion, garlic or any other vegetables, and one or two eggs. Mix everything well. If you want to 'stretch' the minced food, don't add breadcrumbs or flour: use rolled oats or mashed red lentils instead. Allow the mixture to rest for about 20 minutes, or for several hours, in the refrigerator. Shape the mixture into balls or patties and cook them over a low heat in a non-stick frying pan until they are cooked through. At a low temperature, flavours will develop better and the need for salt and fat will be reduced.

Simple desserts

Choose low-glycaemic, fibre-rich fruit such as apples, pears, citrus fruits, raspberries, blackberries, strawberries, grapes, cherries, kiwi fruit, plums, peaches, nectarines or melons. Try:

▶ Mixed strawberries, raspberries and blueberries
▶ Green grapes, sliced kiwi fruit and melon balls
▶ Orange slices sprinkled with cinnamon
▶ Strawberries sprinkled with a little black pepper or balsamic vinegar
▶ Mashing, puréeing or stewing fruit (with spices and fructose if you like) to make fruit soup
▶ Puréeing fruit to make a sauce to go with ricotta, yogurt or ice cream
▶ Natural yogurt with fruit; it's filling and healthy
▶ Unsweetened yogurt flavoured with vanilla essence and fructose. Swirl through some crushed berries, or sprinkle with chopped walnuts or pistachios and drizzle with honey.

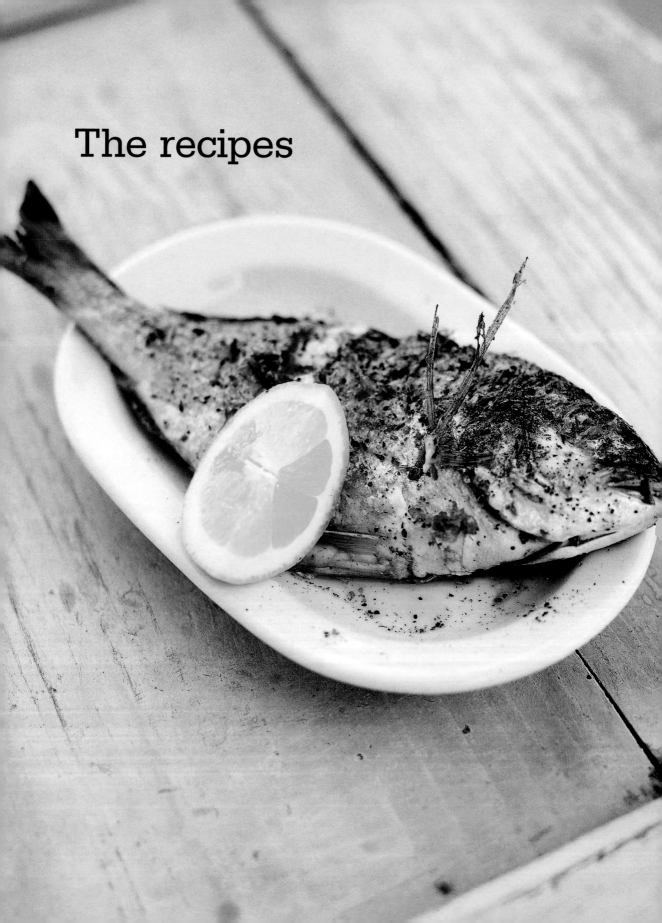

The recipes

Before you begin cooking any of the recipes please note the following:

▶ When a recipe includes salt, I recommend that you use low-sodium or reduced-sodium salt. Most of us consume far more salt than we need – we require only about 1 g of salt a day, yet the average intake is far higher. If you gradually reduce the amount of salt you add to your food you will begin to taste far more of the natural flavours of the ingredients and will soon get into the habit of using less.

▶ Unless a recipe states otherwise, 'pepper' means freshly ground black pepper from the mill.

▶ Where a recipe includes olive oil, this refers to extra virgin olive oil. 'Extra virgin' means that the oil is cold pressed in a natural way and has not been processed at high temperatures.

▶ If you do not use your own homemade stock for recipes, use low-sodium stock, which is available in some supermarkets. Alternatively, use vegetable bouillon powder, which is available in health food shops and some supermarkets.

▶ Many of the recipes that are oven-cooked are heated at a low temperature. This produces lovely succulent meat, poultry or fish (see page 53). However, it is best to use a core temperature/meat thermometer to ensure the meat is cooked all the way through. If you do not have a thermometer, pierce the thickest part of the meat with a thin metal skewer and if the juices run clear it is cooked.

▶ Where a recipe includes a 'make ahead' symbol this indicates that the dish can be refrigerated or frozen. Unless the instructions state otherwise, all dishes should be placed in an airtight container prior to chilling or freezing, and if frozen, thoroughly defrosted before being reheated.

▶ At the end of each recipe you will find the nutritional information. The Glycaemic Load (GL) per serving has been calculated based on the total carbohydrate amount in grams, multiplied by the Glycaemic Index (GI) of the main blood-sugar-influencing ingredient(s) and divided by 100. If the carbohydrate source is solely very low-glycaemic vegetables, the GL is practically zero. Since many of the recipes in this book include significant amounts of protein and/or fat, and also lemon juice or yogurt – all known to reduce the GI and thus the GL – they have a very low GL of less than 6.5 per serving. There are of course a number of recipes that include higher GL carbs; these are designed to be part of your 'reward' meal of the day.

◄ Cucumber soup with prawns

SERVES 4

2 cucumbers
400 ml (14 fl oz) chicken stock
150 ml (5 fl oz) crème fraîche or
sour cream (20% fat)
juice of ½ lemon
salt and pepper

MARINATED PRAWNS

200 g (7 oz) fresh cooked prawns
½ red chilli, finely chopped
1 cm (½ in) piece of fresh ginger,
finely chopped
3 tablespoons sweet chilli sauce
2 sprigs of dill, finely chopped

*A refreshing summer first course, with hot and spicy prawns
as a source of protein.*

1 Peel the cucumbers and chop roughly. Using a food processor or
hand-held blender, blend the cucumbers, stock, cream and lemon juice
until completely smooth. Season to taste with salt and pepper, then
cover and chill for at least 2 hours.

2 Mix the chilli, ginger, chilli sauce and dill and season to taste. Add the
mixture to the prawns and leave to marinate in a cool place for 1 hour.

3 Serve the soup in chilled soup plates. Add the marinated prawns
just before serving.

PER SERVING GLYCAEMIC LOAD 0; PROTEIN 16 G; CARBOHYDRATES 9 G; FAT 9 G
(OF WHICH SATURATES 5 G); FIBRE 2 G

Greek fish soup

SERVES 6

6 tablespoons olive oil
1 onion, chopped
90 g (3 oz) leeks (white
part), chopped
½ fennel bulb, chopped
3 parsley stalks
1 bay leaf
2 sprigs fresh thyme or
1 teaspoon dried thyme
450 ml (15 fl oz) dry white wine
700 ml (1¼ pints) water
salt and pepper
500 g (about 1 lb) fresh
mussels in their shells
500 g (about 1 lb) uncooked
prawns in their shells
1.5 kg (3½ lb) fish – 3 or
4 different types

*This Greek version of bouillabaisse is known as fisherman's soup
or kakavia. It is traditionally made from a mixture of different types
of fish and shellfish – the catch of the day!*

1 Heat the oil over a low heat in a large saucepan. Add the onion and
cook for 10 minutes, or until the onion is soft but not coloured. Add the
leeks, fennel, herbs, wine and water and bring to the boil. Add a pinch
of salt, reduce the heat and simmer for 45 minutes.

2 Meanwhile, clean the mussels thoroughly, discarding any that are
open or have broken shells. Rinse and shell the prawns. Cut the fish into
smallish pieces and sprinkle lightly with salt. Set aside for 10–20 minutes.

3 Strain the vegetable liquid through a sieve into a clean saucepan,
pressing down on the vegetables to extract as much liquid as possible.
Bring the vegetable stock back to the boil, then reduce the heat, add
the fish and simmer for 5–10 minutes. Add the mussels and simmer for
a further 5 minutes, or until all the shells are open. Add the prawns and
simmer for a minute or two, until they are opaque. Season to taste
with salt and pepper and serve at once.

PER SERVING GLYCAEMIC LOAD 0; PROTEIN 55 G; CARBOHYDRATES 2 G; FAT 14 G
(OF WHICH SATURATES 2 G); FIBRE 1 G

Greek vegetable soup

SERVES 4

6 tablespoons olive oil

2 onions, finely chopped

2 garlic cloves, crushed

200 g (7 oz) green cabbage, shredded

3 carrots, diced

3 sticks of celery, chopped

300 g (10½ oz) cooked or canned chickpeas, rinsed

2 litres (3½ pints) vegetable stock or water

400 g (14 oz) can chopped tomatoes

4 tablespoons chopped parsley

salt and pepper

50 g (1¾ oz) feta cheese, crumbled

A substantial and satisfying soup, with protein from the chickpeas and feta cheese.

1 Put the olive oil in a large saucepan over low heat, add the onions and garlic, cover and sweat for 10 minutes, or until the onions are soft but not coloured. Add the cabbage and continue to cook for another 5 minutes.

2 Add the carrots, celery and chickpeas, stir well and cook until the vegetables begin to soften.

3 Add the stock or water and stir well. Increase the heat and bring the soup to the boil. Cover the pan and leave the soup to simmer for 30 minutes. Add the tomatoes and a little salt and pepper and simmer for another 20 minutes.

4 Stir in the parsley, then ladle the soup into bowls or soup plates. Sprinkle the feta cheese over the soup and serve hot. If you like, sprinkle in a few drops of olive oil.

PER SERVING GLYCAEMIC LOAD 7; PROTEIN 11 G; CARBOHYDRATES 27 G; FAT 21 G (OF WHICH SATURATES 4 G); FIBRE 7 G

 MAKE AHEAD Prepare up to step 3 and store in the refrigerator for up to 3 days. This soup can also be frozen.

Broccoli and cauliflower soup

SERVES 6

1 head of broccoli
1 cauliflower
3 tablespoons olive oil
½ onion, sliced
1 litre (1¾ pints) water or stock
salt and pepper
100 ml (3½ fl oz) single cream,
fromage frais or natural yogurt

This comforting, pale green soup is packed with vitamins and minerals, quick to make and very versatile. Chopped fresh herbs are a tasty addition to the basic recipe. Just before serving you could also add a few drops of extra virgin olive oil or cold-pressed flaxseed, pumpkin or avocado oil – do not boil the soup after you have added the oil. To make a light meal, add some protein: shredded cooked chicken, strips of ham, chopped boiled egg or a poached egg.

1 Wash the broccoli and cauliflower and cut into small florets.

2 Heat the olive oil in a large saucepan over low heat, add the onion and cook until soft. Add the broccoli and cauliflower and cook for a few minutes. Add the water or stock and simmer until the vegetables are just tender, 8–10 minutes.

3 Blend in a food processor, or with a hand-held blender, until smooth. Season to taste. Stir in the cream, fromage frais or yogurt, or pour the soup into bowls and swirl the cream on top.

PER SERVING GLYCAEMIC LOAD 0; PROTEIN 6 G; CARBOHYDRATES 5 G; FAT 10 G (OF WHICH SATURATES 3 G); FIBRE 3 G

 MAKE AHEAD This can be made a day in advance – but do not add the cream. Store in the refrigerator.

Rich tomato soup

SERVES 4

1 tablespoon clarified butter

1 small onion, finely chopped

500 g (about 1 lb) tomatoes, chopped

2 x 400 g (14 oz) cans chopped tomatoes

500 ml (18 fl oz) vegetable stock

½ red chilli, seeded and chopped

1 tablespoon chopped fresh thyme leaves

2 tablespoons chopped fresh parsley (plus a little extra, to garnish)

1 garlic clove, finely chopped

1 ripe avocado, peeled and diced (reserve a little, to garnish)

2 tablespoons grated Parmesan (optional)

salt and pepper

pinch of fructose

1 tablespoon olive oil

Tomatoes are packed with lycopene, a micronutrient with potent anti-cancer properties. To serve this as a light meal, add a source of protein, such as cubed turkey or chicken, cooked prawns, steamed fish fillets or 1 or 2 halved boiled eggs per person.

1 Heat the butter in a large saucepan, add the onion and cook until soft. Add the fresh tomatoes, stir well, then add the canned tomatoes and stock and simmer for about 15 minutes.

2 Reduce the heat to very low and blend with a hand-held blender. Add the chilli, herbs, garlic, avocado and Parmesan, if using, and blend again. Add salt, pepper and fructose to taste. Serve in warmed bowls, with the olive oil and a little parsley and avocado spooned on top.

PER SERVING GLYCAEMIC LOAD 0; PROTEIN 7 G; CARBOHYDRATES 13 G; FAT 15 G (OF WHICH SATURATES 5 G); FIBRE 4 G

MAKE AHEAD Make the basis of the soup (step 1) a day ahead. Reheat until piping hot, then stir in the chilli and other flavourings. This soup can be frozen, but this should be done after step 1.

Mushroom soup with goats' cheese

SERVES 4

500 g (1 lb 2 oz) mushrooms

1 tablespoon clarified butter

1 small onion or
2 shallots, chopped

1 garlic clove, finely chopped

1 tablespoon fresh thyme leaves
or ½ teaspoon dried thyme

800 ml (28 fl oz) vegetable or
chicken stock

200 ml (7 fl oz) single cream

100 g (3½ oz) goats'
cheese, rind removed

1 ripe avocado

salt and pepper

200 g (7 oz) smoked ham,
cut into thin strips

fresh herbs or herb
oil (page 68), to garnish

Rich, autumnal mushroom soup becomes a complete meal with the addition of goats' cheese. Vegetarians could omit the ham and use extra cheese. Use any type of mushrooms for this soup: you could use half cultivated mushrooms and half wild. You can also add a handful of dried mushrooms to boost the flavour: soak them in hot water for 30 minutes before starting the recipe.

1 Clean the mushrooms; if they are very dirty you may need to rinse them. Chop or slice, then set aside about half the mushrooms.

2 Melt half the butter in a large saucepan and add half the mushrooms, the onion or shallots and garlic. Cook over medium heat until golden brown, then add the thyme and cook for a few more minutes. Add the stock and cream and simmer for 5 minutes.

3 Crumble the cheese into the soup and leave to melt over a low heat.

4 Peel and chop the avocado and add to the soup, then blend until completely smooth, using a hand-held blender or food processor. Season to taste.

5 Cook the remaining mushrooms in a frying pan with the rest of the butter. Pour the hot soup into 4 warmed bowls. Put some of the mushrooms and ham into each bowl and sprinkle with fresh herbs or a few drops of herb oil.

PER SERVING GLYCAEMIC LOAD 0; PROTEIN 18 G; CARBOHYDRATES 6 G; FAT 26 G (OF WHICH SATURATES 14 G); FIBRE 3 G

 MAKE AHEAD Prepare up to end of step 2, then store in the refrigerator for up to 2 days or freeze.

Gazpacho

SERVES 4

500 ml (18 fl oz) tomato juice
200 ml (7 fl oz) vegetable stock
2 shallots, finely chopped
1 cucumber, peeled and grated
1 small green pepper (capsicum), finely chopped
1 small red pepper (capsicum), finely chopped
½ green chilli, seeds removed, finely chopped
2 tablespoons chopped flat-leaf parsley
1 garlic clove, chopped
1 teaspoon Worcestershire sauce
1 teaspoon fructose
1 tablespoon olive oil
1 teaspoon cold-pressed flaxseed oil
1–2 drops Tabasco sauce
½ teaspoon salt
black pepper

GARNISH

1 tomato, finely diced
1 tablespoon finely chopped chives
45 g (1½ oz) feta cheese, crumbled

My version of the Spanish classic. Some people serve the garnishes in small bowls; optional garnishes include chopped spring onions or chives, chopped hard-boiled eggs and finely diced cucumber.

1 Put half the tomato juice in a food processor with the stock, shallots, cucumber, peppers, chilli, parsley, garlic, Worcestershire sauce, fructose and olive oil. Blend until smooth. Add more tomato juice to get the consistency you want. Place in the refrigerator for at least 2 hours.

2 To serve, stir in the flaxseed oil, Tabasco, salt, and pepper to taste. Pour into chilled bowls and add a few ice cubes if you wish. Garnish with the diced tomato, chives and feta.

PER SERVING GLYCAEMIC LOAD 2; PROTEIN 6 G; CARBOHYDRATES 12 G; FAT 6 G (OF WHICH SATURATES 2 G); FIBRE 3 G

 MAKE AHEAD Prepare step 1 and store the soup for up to 2 days in the refrigerator.

Provençal chicken and vegetable soup

SERVES 4

1 leek
2 carrots
1 stick of celery
1 courgette (zucchini)
10 green beans
4 large ripe tomatoes
2 tablespoons clarified butter
2 sprigs thyme or
½ teaspoon dried thyme
1 bay leaf
1 litre (1¾ pints) chicken stock
4 chicken breasts, skinned
and cut into thin strips
salt and pepper

PISTOU

large bunch of basil
2 garlic cloves
2 tablespoons freshly
grated Parmesan
100 ml (3½ fl oz) olive oil
salt and pepper

Inspired by a classic vegetable soup from the south of France, this is a light version that includes chicken for a good balance of protein and carbohydrates – and it's ready in 15 minutes! A swirl of basil and garlic pistou is an aromatic finishing touch; use ready-made pesto if you like.

1 Cut the vegetables into 1 cm (½ in) cubes or lengths. Heat the butter in a large saucepan and add all the vegetables except the tomatoes. Add 3 tablespoons water and cover with a lid. Cook gently until the water has evaporated, then add the thyme, bay leaf and stock. Bring to the boil, then simmer until the vegetables are tender.

2 Meanwhile make the pistou. Put the basil, garlic and Parmesan into a food processor and blend briefly. With the machine running, gradually add the olive oil, blending until smooth. Season to taste.

3 Add the chicken to the soup and simmer for a further 3–4 minutes, until the chicken is cooked through. Stir in as much of the pistou as you want, then add the tomatoes and season to taste.

PER SERVING GLYCAEMIC LOAD 2; PROTEIN 32 G; CARBOHYDRATES 7 G; FAT 38 G
(OF WHICH SATURATES 11 G); FIBRE 3 G

MAKE AHEAD Make double quantities of soup (step 1) and freeze for up to 1 month. Reheat from frozen until piping hot, then add the chicken and cook through; add tomatoes just before serving. Pistou can be made up to 4 days ahead and stored in the refrigerator.

Chickpea soup with herb oil and feta cheese

SERVES 4

3 tablespoons olive oil

1 large onion, chopped

350 g (12 oz) dried chickpeas, soaked overnight

1 tablespoon cornflour

juice of 1 lemon

3 tablespoons chopped flat-leaf parsley

salt and pepper

50 g (1¾ oz) feta cheese, crumbled

HERB OIL

100 ml (3½ fl oz) olive oil

1 large bunch fresh herbs (e.g. basil, thyme, coriander), chopped

50 g (1¾ oz) Parmesan cheese, grated

Serve a crisp green salad on the side to make this substantial soup into a complete meal. Instead of feta cheese, you could sprinkle finely grated Parmesan as a finishing touch.

1 Heat the olive oil in a large saucepan over low heat, add the onions and cook until they begin to turn golden. Rinse the chickpeas in a colander and add to the saucepan. Add enough water to cover the chickpeas by about 5 cm (2 in) and bring to the boil. Reduce the heat and simmer, skimming occasionally, until the chickpeas are very tender, about 1½ hours.

2 Meanwhile, make the herb oil. Blend the olive oil, herbs and Parmesan with a hand-held blender until they form a coarse, pesto-like paste.

3 Mix the cornflour with the lemon juice and stir into the soup. Add the parsley and a little salt and pepper, to taste. Transfer 2 ladlefuls of the soup to a deep bowl and blend briefly with a hand-held blender; the chickpeas should be crushed, not puréed. Stir this back into the soup.

4 Serve the soup in warmed bowls, sprinkled with a little feta cheese and some of the herb oil.

PER SERVING GLYCAEMIC LOAD 13; PROTEIN 23 G; CARBOHYDRATES 52 G; FAT 27 G (OF WHICH SATURATES 6 G); FIBRE 10 G

 MAKE AHEAD This soup can be stored in the refrigerator for up to 3 days. It also freezes well for up to 3 months.

Greek bean soup

SERVES 6

200 g (7 oz) cannellini beans or other dried white beans, soaked for 12–14 hours

2.5 litres (4½ pints) strong chicken or vegetable stock

2 bay leaves

1 mild onion, finely chopped

2 garlic cloves, crushed

2 carrots, diced

1 stick of celery, finely chopped (reserve any leaves to garnish)

200 g (7 oz) plum tomatoes, peeled, seeded and chopped into cubes, or chopped canned tomatoes

juice of 1 lemon

6 tablespoons olive oil

salt and pepper

1 teaspoon cold-pressed flaxseed oil (optional)

4–6 tablespoons finely chopped flat-leaf parsley

In Greece, this is known as fassoláda, *and for most Greeks it's the closest thing to a national dish.*

1 Drain the beans and put them in a large saucepan. Add the stock and the bay leaves. Bring to the boil, then reduce the heat and simmer for 1½ hours.

2 Turn down the heat and add the onion, garlic, carrots and celery. Simmer for a further 30 minutes.

3 Add the tomatoes, lemon juice and half the olive oil. Season with salt and pepper. Simmer for a further 30 minutes, or until the beans are very soft.

4 Remove from the heat, taste and adjust the seasoning. Ladle into bowls and drizzle over the remaining olive oil and flaxseed oil. Sprinkle with parsley and garnish with celery leaves if you wish. Serve hot.

PER SERVING GLYCAEMIC LOAD 6; PROTEIN 8 G; CARBOHYDRATES 22 G; FAT 12 G (OF WHICH SATURATES 2 G); FIBRE 5 G

 MAKE AHEAD If anything, this improves with being made a day ahead. Or make double quantities and freeze for up to 3 months.

Lentil soup with avocado and turkey

SERVES 4

300 g (10½ oz) dried green lentils
1 litre (1¾ pints) chicken or
vegetable stock
4 tablespoons olive oil
1 onion, finely chopped
2 garlic cloves, finely chopped
2 tablespoons fresh thyme
(or 1 tablespoon dried)
1 ripe avocado,
peeled and chopped
a little lemon juice
salt and pepper
200 g (7 oz) cooked turkey
breast, cut into thin strips
2–3 tablespoons torn fresh basil

Lentils are very nutritious – a good source of protein and fibre, as well as important minerals such as iron, zinc and magnesium. The turkey adds a considerable amount of extra protein, to make a soup that is also a meal. Instead of the turkey, you could add 100 g (3½ oz) crumbled grilled lean bacon or feta cheese. You could also include sun-dried tomatoes, or roasted tomatoes (see page 135).

1 Rinse the lentils thoroughly in a colander, then place in a large saucepan, add the stock and bring to the boil. Reduce the heat and simmer until the lentils are soft, 25–35 minutes.

2 Put half the olive oil in a saucepan over low heat, add the onions and garlic, cover and sweat for 10 minutes, until the onions are translucent. Add the thyme and stir until fragrant.

3 Add to the pan with the lentils, then blend briefly with a hand-held blender: do not overblend. Add the avocado and blend again. If the soup is too thick, add a little stock or water. Season to taste with lemon juice, salt and pepper.

4 Place the turkey breast in 4 warmed soup plates and pour in the hot soup. Drizzle the remaining olive oil onto the soup, then add the basil and serve at once.

PER SERVING GLYCAEMIC LOAD 9; PROTEIN 35 G; CARBOHYDRATES 40 G; FAT 18 G (OF WHICH SATURATES 3 G); FIBRE 8 G

MAKE AHEAD This freezes well, so why not make a double quantity – but do not add the avocado and turkey until you are ready to serve. Alternatively, store in the refrigerator for up to 3 days.

Avocado foam with chicken

SERVES 4

4 chicken breasts, about
150 g (5½ oz) each
2 tablespoons olive oil
salt and pepper
2 tablespoons chopped
fresh herbs (e.g. basil, dill,
coriander, parsley) – optional
1 tablespoon clarified butter
1 small onion or
2 shallots, chopped
½ teaspoon curry powder
1 tablespoon chopped fresh
thyme or ½ teaspoon dried thyme
½ red chilli, seeds removed,
finely chopped
800 ml (28 fl oz) chicken stock
200 ml (7 fl oz) single cream
2 ripe avocados
½ teaspoon fructose
fresh herbs or herb oil
(see page 68), to serve

*This gently spiced soup, with a generous helping of chicken,
is a meal in itself. Cooking chicken at a low temperature gives
a tender, juicy result.*

1 Preheat the oven to 120°C/250°F/gas ½ or the lowest setting. Brown
the chicken in a little oil in a non-stick frying pan. Season the chicken
with a little salt and pepper and place in a non-stick roasting tin with
the herbs, if using. Cook for 30–35 minutes, or until the juices run
clear when the chicken is tested with a thin skewer.

2 Meanwhile, melt the butter in a saucepan over low heat, add the
onion or shallots and cook until translucent. Add the curry powder,
thyme and chilli and cook for a further minute. Add the stock and
cream and simmer for 5 minutes.

3 Peel and chop the avocados and add to the soup, along with
the fructose. Use a hand-held blender to blend the soup until it is
completely smooth and foamy. Season to taste with salt and pepper.

4 Slice the chicken into thin strips and place in 4 warmed deep soup
plates. Pour the warm soup around the chicken and sprinkle with fresh
herbs or a few drops of herb oil.

PER SERVING GLYCAEMIC LOAD 0; PROTEIN 29 G; CARBOHYDRATES 5 G; FAT 27 G
(OF WHICH SATURATES 12 G); FIBRE 2 G

Salade niçoise with grilled seafood

SERVES 4

1 lollo rosso or Cos (Romaine)
lettuce, leaves separated

300 g (10½ oz) tuna fillet,
cut into 4 pieces

1 yellow courgette (zucchini),
cut into 5 mm (¼ in) slices

12 large scallops, shelled

8 large prawns or langoustines,
peeled and halved lengthways

200 g (7 oz) thin French
beans, halved

1 tablespoon olive oil

1 red pepper (capsicum),
deseeded and cut into strips

200 g (7 oz) yellow or red
cherry tomatoes, quartered

90 g (3 oz) green olives, stoned
and halved lengthways

DRESSING

3 tablespoons red wine vinegar

1 tablespoon Dijon mustard

1 tablespoon anchovy paste

½ teaspoon dried thyme

½ teaspoon fructose

5 tablespoons olive oil

An impressive and colourful main course salad. If you can't obtain langoustines you could use squid. Choose tender squid no more than 10–12 cm (4–5 in) long, cut off the tentacles and rinse the body pouch, then cut it down one side and score the surface with criss-cross lines before grilling. Instead of tuna, you could use fillets of red mullet.

1 Immerse the lettuce leaves in a large bowl of cold water and leave to crisp up for a few minutes, then drain and dry well (use a salad spinner if you have one).

2 Meanwhile, combine the dressing ingredients in a small bowl and emulsify with a hand-held blender. Alternatively, shake the ingredients together in a screwtop jar.

3 Place the tuna and courgette on a baking tray and brush on both sides with about 2 tablespoons of the dressing. Put the scallops and prawns or langoustines in a bowl and mix with another 2 tablespoons of dressing. Leave both to marinate for at least 15 minutes.

4 Drop the French beans into a pan of boiling water and blanch for about 3 minutes. Drain in a colander and rinse under cold water until cooled. Transfer the beans to a bowl and add 2 tablespoons of the dressing. Set aside.

5 Heat the olive oil in a frying pan and fry the pepper over a moderate heat until soft. Leave to cool.

6 Prepare the barbecue. (If cooking indoors, preheat the grill to high or heat a ridged grill pan or heavy frying pan.) Barbecue all the seafood for about 2 minutes on each side.

7 Make a bed of lettuce leaves on 4 plates. Divide the scallops, prawns, tuna, courgette, beans, red pepper, tomatoes and olives among the plates. Spoon a little dressing over each plate and serve the rest separately.

PER SERVING GLYCAEMIC LOAD 0; PROTEIN 34 G; CARBOHYDRATES 10 G; FAT 31 G
(OF WHICH SATURATES 5 G); FIBRE 4 G

Smoked salmon, cauliflower and chickpea salad

SERVES 4

1 small cauliflower, separated into florets

400 g (14 oz) can chickpeas, drained and rinsed

150 g (5½ oz) smoked salmon, cut into strips

2 hard-boiled eggs, sliced or roughly chopped

DRESSING

75 g (2½ oz) fromage frais

2 tablespoons olive oil

small bunch of fresh dill, chopped

juice of 1 lemon

½ teaspoon fructose

salt and pepper

A delicious protein-rich salad, this makes the perfect lunch or dinner when time is at a premium.

1 Cook the cauliflower in plenty of lightly salted boiling water until it is just tender but still firm. Tip the florets into a colander and drain well. Leave to cool.

2 Mix together the ingredients for the dressing. Season with salt and pepper.

3 Combine the cauliflower and chickpeas in a salad bowl and add the smoked salmon and eggs. Pour over the dressing and mix everything together gently. Sprinkle with a little more chopped dill, if liked, and serve at once.

PER SERVING GLYCAEMIC LOAD 1; PROTEIN 23 G; CARBOHYDRATES 18 G; FAT 14 G (OF WHICH SATURATES 3 G); FIBRE 5 G

Tuna, chickpea and avocado salad

SERVES 4

2 avocados

400 g (14 oz) can tuna in water, drained and flaked

400 g (14 oz) can chickpeas, drained and rinsed

1 red onion, cut into thin wedges

2 tablespoons finely chopped gherkins

1 tablespoon chopped fresh dill

DRESSING

2 tablespoons white wine vinegar

4 tablespoons olive oil

1 teaspoon Dijon mustard

½ teaspoon fructose

2 tablespoons freshly grated Parmesan

salt and pepper

This salad is simplicity itself, but for an even quicker tuna salad, mix the tuna with hard-boiled egg, finely chopped onion and gherkins, and a few tablespoons of fromage frais.

1 Mix together the ingredients for the dressing, using a hand-held blender if you have one. Season with salt and pepper.

2 Halve the avocados and remove the stones. Spoon out the flesh and cut into dice.

3 Combine the tuna, avocado, chickpeas, red onion, gherkins and dill in a salad bowl. Pour over the dressing and gently mix everything together.

PER SERVING GLYCAEMIC LOAD 4; PROTEIN 34 G; CARBOHYDRATES 18 G; FAT 26 G (OF WHICH SATURATES 6 G); FIBRE 6 G

Chicken, aubergine and mint salad

SERVES 4

1 tablespoon melted
clarified butter

4 skinless boneless chicken breasts

salt and pepper

1 aubergine (eggplant), cut into
1 cm (½ in) slices

2 spring onions, thinly sliced

large handful of fresh mint leaves

2 tablespoons sunflower
seeds, toasted

DRESSING

3 tablespoons fructose

2 tablespoons fish sauce

2 garlic cloves, finely chopped

1 green chilli, deseeded
and thinly sliced

juice of 4 limes

4 tablespoons olive oil

1 lemon grass stalk, outer
layers peeled off, finely
chopped (optional)

1 small onion, finely chopped

Aubergine and mint are typically Mediterranean ingredients, but the spicy-salty-sour dressing is inspired by Thai food.

1 Preheat the oven to 120°C/250°F/gas ½ or the lowest setting. Heat a ridged grill pan, then brush with half of the melted butter. Season the chicken breasts with a little salt and pepper and char-grill until they are seared and patterned with char marks on both sides.

2 Transfer the chicken breasts to a roasting tin and place in the oven. Bake for about 25–30 minutes, or until cooked through; the juices should run clear when the chicken is tested with a thin skewer. Allow to cool until just warm.

3 Wipe out the grill pan, then brush with the remaining butter. Char-grill the aubergine slices until tender, turning to cook both sides evenly. Remove from the pan and leave to cool.

4 To make the dressing, combine the fructose, fish sauce, garlic, chilli, lime juice and olive oil in a bowl and mix well. Stir in the lemon grass and onion.

5 Cut or tear the cooked chicken into strips and dice the aubergines. Place both in a serving dish with the spring onions and pour over the dressing. Cover and leave to stand for 30 minutes so the flavours can develop and blend.

6 Sprinkle the mint leaves and toasted sunflower seeds on top and serve.

PER SERVING GLYCAEMIC LOAD 4; PROTEIN 29 G; CARBOHYDRATES 22 G; FAT 23 G (OF WHICH SATURATES 6 G); FIBRE 2 G

◄ Chicken, walnut and red bean salad

SERVES 4

1 ripe avocado

400 g (14 oz) can red kidney beans, drained and rinsed

400 g (14 oz) cooked chicken, roughly chopped

1 small red onion, thinly sliced

75 g (2½ oz) wild rocket

1 small lollo rosso or other red lettuce, torn into pieces if large

2 ripe tomatoes, cut into chunks

50 g (1¾ oz) walnuts

DRESSING

juice of 1 lemon

3 tablespoons olive oil

1 tablespoon balsamic vinegar

1 tablespoon soy sauce

1 tablespoon French mustard

1 teaspoon fructose

salt and pepper

This is a satisfying and versatile main course salad. Instead of lollo rosso you could use baby spinach; instead of red beans, try chickpeas; and if you don't like walnuts, substitute a thinly sliced small leek, which will give a delicate crunch to the salad.

1 Halve the avocado, remove the stone and peel off the skin. (The easiest way to do this is to use a spoon and insert it just inside the skin; slide the spoon all around to remove the flesh.) Cut the avocado flesh into small dice.

2 Combine the avocado with all the other ingredients for the salad, except the walnuts, in a salad bowl.

3 Stir the ingredients for the dressing together, or shake them in a screwtop jar. Add to the salad and mix together gently. Sprinkle with the walnuts.

PER SERVING GLYCAEMIC LOAD 5; PROTEIN 36 G; CARBOHYDRATES 21 G; FAT 27 G (OF WHICH SATURATES 4 G); FIBRE 8 G

Tomato salad with beans and basil

SERVES 4

500 g (1 lb 2 oz) ripe tomatoes, cut into largish pieces

1 onion, finely chopped

500 g (1 lb 2 oz) cooked or canned black beans or chickpeas (drain and rinse canned beans well)

DRESSING

large bunch of fresh basil, coarsely chopped

2 garlic cloves, chopped

100 ml (3½ fl oz) olive oil

2 tablespoons white balsamic vinegar or white wine vinegar

pinch of fructose, or to taste

salt and pepper

Serve this with cold ham or turkey to make a satisfying meal. An excellent variation is to scatter a little chopped avocado on top just before serving.

1 Combine the tomatoes, onion and beans or chickpeas in a salad bowl.

2 Put the dressing ingredients in a tall narrow bowl and blend with a hand-held blender. Alternatively, whizz in a food processor. Season with salt and pepper.

3 Pour the dressing over the salad and mix gently but thoroughly. Leave for a while before serving so the flavours can blend.

PER SERVING GLYCAEMIC LOAD 6; PROTEIN 10 G; CARBOHYDRATES 27 G; FAT 26 G (OF WHICH SATURATES 4 G); FIBRE 7 G

Italian bean salad

SERVES 4

75 g (2½ oz) wild rocket

400 g (14 oz) can artichoke hearts, drained, rinsed and cut into small pieces

400 g (14 oz) can red kidney beans, drained and rinsed

100 g (3½ oz) roast turkey breast, cut into strips

100 g (3½ oz) cooked ham, cut into strips

3 large, ripe tomatoes, diced

4 hard-boiled eggs, quartered

2 tablespoons toasted sunflower seeds

DRESSING

2 tablespoons white wine vinegar

3 tablespoons olive oil

3 tablespoons water

2 garlic cloves, crushed

1 tablespoon chopped fresh oregano or 1 teaspoon dried oregano

2 tablespoons chopped fresh parsley

This main course salad is perfect for a summer buffet.

1 Rinse and drain the rocket leaves, if necessary. Combine in a salad bowl with the artichoke hearts, beans, turkey, ham and tomatoes.

2 Mix together the dressing ingredients by whizzing them with a hand-held blender or shaking them in a screwtop jar.

3 Garnish the salad with the eggs and sprinkle with the sunflower seeds. Pour the dressing over the salad or serve it alongside.

PER SERVING GLYCAEMIC LOAD 6; PROTEIN 29 G; CARBOHYDRATES 20 G; FAT 20 G (OF WHICH SATURATES 4 G); FIBRE 8 G

White bean salad

A good alternative to potato salad, this goes really well with cured meats. For a spicy kick, add a little finely chopped red chilli.

1 Drain the beans, then put them into a saucepan with plenty of fresh cold water. Bring to the boil and simmer until completely soft; this will take around 1 hour. Drain the beans in a colander and then refresh under cold running water.

2 Put the beans in a large bowl and add the onion, gherkins, sun-dried tomatoes and chives or leek.

3 Mix together the dressing ingredients and season with salt and pepper. Pour the dressing over the bean mixture and fold everything together. Transfer the salad to a serving dish.

PER SERVING GLYCAEMIC LOAD 10; PROTEIN 16 G; CARBOHYDRATES 37 G; FAT 12 G (OF WHICH SATURATES 2 G); FIBRE 8 G

SERVES 4

250 g (9 oz) dried butter beans or other large white beans, soaked overnight

1 red or white onion, finely chopped

2 tablespoons finely chopped gherkins

40 g (1¼ oz) sun-dried tomatoes, cut into thin strips

2 tablespoons chopped fresh chives, or ½ leek, thinly sliced

DRESSING

75 g (2½ oz) fromage frais (ideally 1% fat)

2 tablespoons crème fraîche or sour cream (20% fat)

1 tablespoon cold-pressed flaxseed oil

juice of ½ lemon

chopped fresh herbs such as basil and flat-leaf parsley

salt and pepper

Piquant pasta salad with tuna

This is a good mid-week meal as it uses storecupboard ingredients.

1 Cook the pasta in plenty of lightly salted boiling water until al dente. Drain in a colander and set aside to cool.

2 Peel the cucumber, cut it in half lengthways and scrape out the seeds with a teaspoon. Cut the cucumber into strips 4–5 cm (about 2 in) long.

3 Put the fromage frais in a bowl and add the lemon juice, dill, chilli sauce, flaxseed oil (if using) and chopped gherkins. Season with salt and pepper.

4 Combine the pasta, tuna, cucumber, tomatoes and red onion in a large salad bowl. Pour over the dressing and fold together carefully. Sprinkle the capers on top.

PER SERVING GLYCAEMIC LOAD 14; PROTEIN 33 G; CARBOHYDRATES 47 G; FAT 5 G (OF WHICH SATURATES 1 G); FIBRE 4 G

SERVES 4

200 g (7 oz) dried fusilli (preferably wholewheat)

1 cucumber

75 g (2½ oz) fromage frais (1% fat)

juice of ½ lemon

2 tablespoons chopped fresh dill

1 tablespoon sweet chilli sauce

1 tablespoon cold-pressed flaxseed oil (optional)

2 tablespoons chopped gherkins

salt and pepper

400 g (14 oz) can tuna in water, drained and flaked

20 cherry tomatoes, halved

1 red onion, thinly sliced

1 tablespoon capers

Pesto prawn and pasta salad

SERVES 4

150 g (5½ oz) dried fusilli
(preferably wholewheat)
15 g (½ oz) clarified butter
2 sticks of celery, diced
1 green pepper (capsicum),
deseeded and diced
1 red pepper (capsicum),
deseeded and diced
2 spring onions, finely chopped
400 g (14 oz) cooked peeled
prawns, thawed if frozen
unsalted peanuts (optional)

DRESSING

8 tablespoons pesto sauce
(see page 86)
lemon juice

A simple yet incredibly tasty salad.

1 Cook the pasta in plenty of lightly salted boiling water until al dente. Drain in a colander, then rinse with cold running water. Leave the pasta to drain well.

2 Melt the butter in a frying pan, add the celery and peppers, and soften slightly without colouring. Add the spring onions and cook for a further minute or so, then remove the vegetables from the pan and leave to cool to room temperature.

3 Place the pasta, vegetables and prawns in a bowl and mix well. Thin the pesto with a little lemon juice, then pour this dressing over the salad and toss well. Sprinkle over a few peanuts before serving, if liked.

PER SERVING GLYCAEMIC LOAD 13; PROTEIN 29 G; CARBOHYDRATES 32 G; FAT 28 G (OF WHICH SATURATES 6 G); FIBRE 3 G

Avocado, courgette and pasta salad ▶

SERVES 4

300 g (10½ oz) dried fusilli
(preferably wholewheat)
3 tablespoons olive oil
1 courgette (zucchini),
cut into thin strips
2 ripe avocados
2 tablespoons chopped
flat-leaf parsley
grated zest of 1 lemon

DRESSING

2 tablespoons white wine vinegar
4 tablespoons olive oil
1 teaspoon Dijon mustard
½ teaspoon fructose
2 tablespoons freshly
grated Parmesan
1 tablespoon cold-pressed
flaxseed oil (optional)
salt and pepper

Serve with meat or fish. Also good with other dishes as part of a buffet.

1 Cook the pasta in plenty of lightly salted boiling water until al dente. Drain in a colander, then return the pasta to the pan and add 2 tablespoons olive oil, turning the pasta gently to coat with the oil. Leave to cool.

2 Heat the remaining olive oil in a frying pan, add the courgette and cook until soft but not coloured. Remove from the pan and leave to cool.

3 Mix all the dressing ingredients together thoroughly, using a hand-held blender. Season with salt and pepper.

4 Halve the avocados and remove the stones. Spoon out the flesh and cut it into pieces.

5 Place the pasta in a large bowl. Add the avocado and courgette, and pour over the dressing. Add the chopped parsley and lemon zest and gently mix everything together.

PER SERVING GLYCAEMIC LOAD 18; PROTEIN 13 G; CARBOHYDRATES 57 G; FAT 35 G (OF WHICH SATURATES 7 G); FIBRE 4 G

Greek salad

A lazy summer day in Greece... lunch al fresco at a taverna by the sea, a glass of chilled white wine and a Greek salad – life is beautiful.

SERVES 4

Cos (Romaine) lettuce leaves

2 large, ripe tomatoes, preferably sun-ripened

1 cucumber, peeled and sliced

1 red onion, thinly sliced

1 green pepper (capsicum), deseeded and cut into strips

10–15 black olives

125 g (4½ oz) feta cheese, diced

2 teaspoons chopped fresh or dried oregano

DRESSING

100 ml (3½ fl oz) olive oil

3 tablespoons white or red wine vinegar

a little mustard powder

salt and pepper

1 Make the dressing by combining the olive oil, vinegar, mustard and and a little salt and pepper in a screwtop jar. Shake well. Taste the dressing and add more salt and pepper if necessary.

2 Place the lettuce leaves in a salad bowl or on a platter. Arrange the remaining ingredients over the lettuce. Drizzle over some of the dressing and serve the rest alongside.

PER SERVING GLYCAEMIC LOAD 0; PROTEIN 7 G; CARBOHYDRATES 9 G; FAT 30 G (OF WHICH SATURATES 8 G); FIBRE 3 G

Cauliflower and broccoli salad with Parmesan dressing

SERVES 4

1 cauliflower, broken into florets

1 head of broccoli, cut into small florets

50 g (1¾ oz) lean bacon, cut into thin strips

PARMESAN DRESSING

3 tablespoons olive oil

50 g (1¾ oz) Parmesan, finely grated

½ teaspoon fructose

1 teaspoon finely chopped fresh thyme or ½ teaspoon dried thyme

salt and pepper

Don't discard the broccoli stalks; they taste as good as the florets. Thinly peel the stalks and cut across into thick slices. This salad can also be served warm: make the dressing first, then pour it over the hot vegetables and scatter over the hot bacon.

1 Drop the cauliflower and broccoli into a pan of boiling water and blanch for about 2 minutes. Tip the vegetables into a colander to drain, then refresh with cold running water.

2 Fry the bacon in a pan until crisp and the fat runs. Transfer the bacon strips to a plate lined with kitchen paper to drain off excess fat. Leave to cool.

3 Place the ingredients for the dressing in a tall narrow container and mix well using a hand-held blender. Season with salt and pepper.

4 Put the cauliflower and broccoli in a serving dish, pour over some of the dressing and scatter on the bacon strips. Serve the rest of the dressing alongside.

PER SERVING GLYCAEMIC LOAD 0; PROTEIN 17 G; CARBOHYDRATES 6 G; FAT 16 G (OF WHICH SATURATES 5 G); FIBRE 4 G

Curried yogurt dressing

MAKES 6–8 SERVINGS

1 teaspoon curry powder

juice of ½ lemon

200 g (7 oz) natural yogurt

2 tablespoons olive oil

1 cm (½ in) piece of fresh ginger, finely grated

1 teaspoon fructose

a little finely chopped red chilli (optional)

salt and pepper

This dressing will enliven most salads, and goes particularly well with those based on chicken. You can use fromage frais instead of yogurt, if you prefer. Also try adding some chopped fresh herbs such as coriander or lemon thyme as a variation.

1 Stir the curry powder into the lemon juice, then add the remaining ingredients and mix well. Leave the dressing in the refrigerator for an hour before using, to allow the flavours to develop.

TOTAL FOR RECIPE GLYCAEMIC LOAD 2; PROTEIN 10 G; CARBOHYDRATES 21 G; FAT 24 G (OF WHICH SATURATES 4 G); FIBRE 0 G

Tomato, chilli and coriander salsa ▶

MAKES 6–8 SERVINGS

200 g (7 oz) ripe tomatoes, chopped, or chopped canned tomatoes

1 small red onion, finely chopped

2 garlic cloves, finely chopped

1 teaspoon finely chopped red chilli

2 tablespoons chopped fresh coriander

2 tablespoons extra virgin olive oil

1 tablespoon balsamic vinegar

1 teaspoon ground cumin (optional)

salt and pepper

Serve as a first course with other salads and dips, or to accompany grilled or baked fish, chicken or meat. In the winter, or when you can't get really ripe tomatoes, use canned tomatoes. This salsa will taste even better if left in the refrigerator for a few hours before serving.

1 Mix all the ingredients together in a bowl. Season with a little salt and pepper.

TOTAL FOR RECIPE GLYCAEMIC LOAD 1; PROTEIN 4 G; CARBOHYDRATES 18 G; FAT 22 G (OF WHICH SATURATES 3 G); FIBRE 3 G

Aubergine purée ▶

MAKES 4–6 SERVINGS

500 g (1 lb 2 oz) aubergines (eggplants)

15 g (½ oz) clarified butter

50 g (1¾ oz) shallots, finely chopped

1 garlic clove, crushed

100 g (3½ oz) ripe tomatoes, skinned, deseeded and diced

1 heaped teaspoon finely chopped fresh flat-leaf parsley

1 heaped teaspoon finely chopped fresh coriander

3 tablespoons olive oil

2 teaspoons cold-pressed flaxseed oil (optional)

a little freshly squeezed lemon juice

salt and pepper

This can be served warm or at room temperature. Note that the tomatoes must be fresh and ripe – canned will not do here.

1 Preheat the grill to high. Grill the aubergines until the skin is completely black but not charred, turning to colour evenly (you could also do this over a gas ring, with the aubergine pierced on a long-handled metal fork). When they are cool enough to handle, peel off the skin and chop the flesh very finely. Place the aubergine flesh in a bowl.

2 Melt the butter in a frying pan, add the shallots and garlic, and cook until the shallots are softened but not browned. Add the tomatoes and herbs. Cook for 2 minutes to allow the flavours to develop.

3 Tip the tomato and shallot mixture into the bowl with the aubergine. Add the oils and lemon juice and mix it all together. Season with salt and pepper.

TOTAL FOR RECIPE GLYCAEMIC LOAD 1; PROTEIN 6 G; CARBOHYDRATES 18 G; FAT 58 G (OF WHICH SATURATES 14 G); FIBRE 12 G

Pesto sauce

MAKES 6–8 SERVINGS

75 g (2½ oz) pine nuts
90 g (3 oz) fresh basil leaves
3 garlic cloves, crushed
50 g (1¾ oz) Parmesan cheese, freshly grated
300 ml (10 fl oz) olive oil
salt and pepper

This makes a thick pesto. For a thinner consistency, to make a sauce that can be used as a salad dressing, adjust the quantity of oil.

1 Toast the pine nuts lightly in a dry frying pan. They should be just golden but not browned.

2 Put the pine nuts in a food processor, add all the other ingredients and whizz to a smooth sauce. Alternatively, put all the ingredients in a bowl and blend with a hand-held blender. Season with salt and pepper.

TOTAL FOR RECIPE GLYCAEMIC LOAD 0; PROTEIN 33 G; CARBOHYDRATES 4 G; FAT 341 G (OF WHICH SATURATES 52 G); FIBRE 3 G

Mustard and basil dressing

MAKES 8–10 SERVINGS

200 ml (7 fl oz) olive oil
90 g (3 oz) fresh basil, leaves and stalks
3 garlic cloves, finely chopped
2 tablespoons coarse-grain mustard
salt and pepper
pinch of fructose, or to taste

Instead of basil, you can use tarragon or oregano.

1 Combine all the ingredients in a food processor and whizz until smooth. Alternatively, use a hand-held blender. If you have neither, you can chop the basil finely and mix with all the other ingredients in a bowl. Season with salt, pepper and fructose. Leave the dressing to stand for a while before using, to allow the flavours to develop.

TOTAL FOR RECIPE GLYCAEMIC LOAD 0; PROTEIN 5 G; CARBOHYDRATES 6 G; FAT 184 G (OF WHICH SATURATES 25 G); FIBRE 4 G

Avocado dip

MAKES 2–4 SERVINGS

2 ripe avocados
juice of ½ lemon
75 g (2½ oz) fromage frais (8% fat)
¼ red chilli, deseeded and finely chopped
2 garlic cloves, finely chopped
1 shallot, finely chopped
salt and pepper
pinch of fructose, or to taste

Serve as a first course or snack, with sticks of raw vegetables.

1 Halve the avocados and remove the stones. Scoop out the flesh with a tablespoon. Cut out any brown patches.

2 Place the avocado flesh in a bowl and mash it with a fork. It doesn't need to be completely smooth. Mix in the lemon juice.

3 Add the fromage frais, chilli, garlic and shallot and mix well. Season with salt, pepper and fructose.

TOTAL FOR RECIPE GLYCAEMIC LOAD 2; PROTEIN 9 G; CARBOHYDRATES 13 G; FAT 44 G (OF WHICH SATURATES 11 G); FIBRE 7 G

Hummus

MAKES 6–8 SERVINGS

400 g (14 oz) cooked or
canned chickpeas
100 g (3½ oz) tahini
2 garlic cloves, crushed
3 tablespoons olive oil
juice of 1 lemon
salt and pepper
1 teaspoon paprika
a little chopped fresh parsley

*Set the bowl of hummus in the middle of a large dish and arrange
sticks of raw vegetables neatly around it – perfect for a snack.
Hummus can also be spread on bread in place of butter.*

1 If using canned chickpeas, drain and rinse them well. Place the
chickpeas in a food processor or blender and process to a coarse pulp.

2 Stir the tahini with 1–2 tablespoons water, then add to the food
processor along with the garlic and process to mix. With the machine
running, slowly add the olive oil and lemon juice through the hole in the
lid and process to a smooth paste. Season with salt and pepper.

3 Transfer to a serving bowl and sprinkle with the paprika and
chopped parsley.

TOTAL FOR RECIPE GLYCAEMIC LOAD 18; PROTEIN 48 G; CARBOHYDRATES 67 G;
FAT 103 G (OF WHICH SATURATES 14 G); FIBRE 24 G

Tzatziki

MAKES 6–8 SERVINGS

500 g (1 lb 2oz) natural Greek-
style (strained) yogurt
or natural yogurt
2 cucumbers
salt and pepper
3 garlic cloves, finely chopped
3 tablespoons olive oil
a little lemon juice
pinch of fructose, or to taste

*This classic Greek cucumber and yogurt salad (illustrated on page 85)
is good as an accompaniment to grilled fish, or as a dip with raw
mixed vegetables.*

1 If using ordinary yogurt, put the yogurt in a sieve lined with a
coffee filter or muslin and set over a bowl. Leave to drain for at least
2 hours, or, ideally, overnight in the refrigerator. This isn't necessary if
you use Greek-style yogurt, as it has already been drained.

2 Peel the cucumbers and halve lengthways. Scrape out the seeds with
a teaspoon. Coarsely grate the cucumber and mix with a little salt.
Leave for 10–15 minutes, then squeeze out as much liquid from the
cucumber as possible.

3 Add the garlic to the yogurt along with the oil. Mix in the grated
cucumber and season with lemon juice, fructose, salt and pepper.

TOTAL FOR RECIPE GLYCAEMIC LOAD 11; PROTEIN 33 G; CARBOHYDRATES 54 G;
FAT 72 G (OF WHICH SATURATES 28 G); FIBRE 9 G

Mussels with white beans and olives

SERVES 4

300 g (10½ oz) dried white
beans, soaked overnight

1 kg (2¼ lb) fresh
mussels in their shells

4 tablespoons clarified butter

½ onion, finely chopped

180 ml (6 fl oz) dry white wine

2 garlic cloves, finely chopped

400 g (14 oz) can chopped
tomatoes

1 tablespoon finely
chopped fresh coriander

2 tablespoons lemon juice

8 stoned black olives, halved

salt and pepper

¼ teaspoon fructose

2 tablespoons chopped
flat-leaf parsley

*You will love this hearty stew – it is tasty and filling, with just the
right balance of sweet, sour and salty flavours.*

1 Boil the soaked beans in plenty of water until soft.

2 Clean the mussels thoroughly in cold water. Discard any
mussels that are damaged or that do not close when tapped.

3 Melt half the butter in a large saucepan, add the onion and grind
over a little pepper. Fry gently for 1 minute. Add the mussels and
100 ml (3½ fl oz) of the wine. Put on the lid and cook until the mussels
open. Drain the mussels, reserving the cooking liquid. Shell the mussels,
reserving some in their shells, to garnish. Discard any mussels that
have not opened. Cover the mussels to keep them warm.

4 Melt the remaining butter in a saucepan, add the garlic and fry gently.
Add the tomatoes, coriander, the remaining wine, the lemon juice and
olives. Simmer for 5 minutes. Add the mussel stock, beans and mussels.
Place over a low heat to heat everything through. Season to taste with
salt, pepper and fructose. Sprinkle with parsley and serve at once.

PER SERVING GLYCAEMIC LOAD 5; PROTEIN 41 G; CARBOHYDRATES 17 G; FAT 28 G
(OF WHICH SATURATES 10 G); FIBRE 13 G

Grilled squid stuffed with feta cheese

SERVES 4

4 fresh squid, each weighing about 225 g (8 oz)
8 sticks of feta cheese
100 ml (3½ fl oz) olive oil
2 garlic cloves, crushed
4 fresh marjoram leaves, finely chopped
salt and pepper
lemon juice or lemon wedges, to garnish

An unusual but simple dish for a summer barbecue. Serve with tomato salad with beans and basil (page 77) or with herbed quinoa pilaf (page 144).

1 To clean the squid: pull the tentacles gently away from the body. Discard the innards and the hard 'quill'. Trim off and discard the hard part at the top of the tentacles, leaving the tentacles joined together. Wash thoroughly and dry with kitchen paper.

2 Lay the squid and feta cheese in a glass dish just large enough to hold them all side by side. Mix together the olive oil, garlic and marjoram; season to taste with salt and pepper. Pour over the squid and cheese, cover the dish and leave in a cool place for 2–3 hours.

3 Gently push 2 sticks of feta into each squid body. Spear the tentacles onto a skewer.

4 Heat a barbecue or ridged chargrill pan. Brush the grill rack or pan with oil or butter, then add the squid bodies and grill for about 5 minutes. Carefully turn the squid over and grill for a further 2 minutes; the tentacles will also take 2 minutes. Serve at once, with lemon wedges. Alternatively squeeze lemon juice over the squid before serving.

PER SERVING GLYCAEMIC LOAD 0; PROTEIN 35 G; CARBOHYDRATES 0 G; FAT 22 G
(OF WHICH SATURATES 6 G); FIBRE 0 G

Squid with fennel and spinach

1 kg (2¼ lb) fresh squid
120 ml (4 fl oz) olive oil
1 onion, finely chopped
2 fennel bulbs, sliced
90 g (3 oz) spinach, chopped
2 spring onions, sliced
2 ripe tomatoes, diced
salt and pepper
juice of 1 large lemon

If you are short of time, use frozen calamari rings instead of squid.

1 To clean the squid: pull the tentacles gently away from the body. Discard the innards and the hard 'quill'. Trim off and discard the hard part at the top of the tentacles, leaving the tentacles joined together. Wash the squid thoroughly, pat dry and chop roughly.

2 Heat the oil in a large, thick-based saucepan. Add the onion and cook for 2 minutes. Add the squid and stir over the heat until the squid becomes opaque. Add 450 ml (15 fl oz) water, cover with a lid and leave to simmer for 45 minutes.

3 Add the fennel, spinach, spring onions, tomatoes, salt and pepper and mix well. Add more water if necessary. Cover and cook for a further 5–10 minutes until the fennel is tender. Remove from the heat, add the lemon juice and leave to stand for 10–15 minutes before serving.

PER SERVING GLYCAEMIC LOAD 0; PROTEIN 23 G; CARBOHYDRATES 4 G; FAT 18 G (OF WHICH SATURATES 4 G); FIBRE 2 G

Mussel and mushroom fricassée

2 kg (4½ lb) fresh mussels in their shells
2 tablespoons clarified butter
a little white wine (optional)
400 ml (14 fl oz) fish or chicken stock
100 ml (3½ fl oz) single cream
1 tablespoon cornflour (optional)
500 g (1 lb 2 oz) button mushrooms, sliced
salt and pepper
250 g (9 oz) rocket leaves, roughly chopped
1 teaspoon chopped fresh tarragon
1 small bunch chives, chopped
1 tablespoon capers

For a healthy lunch or supper, accompany with a bean or lentil salad.

1 Clean the mussels thoroughly in cold water. Discard any mussels that are damaged or that do not close when tapped.

2 Melt 1 tablespoon butter in a large saucepan over medium-high heat. Add the mussels and put on the lid. When the mussels start to open, pour in the white wine and stock and cook until the mussels have opened. Strain the stock into a clean saucepan and shell the mussels.

3 Add the cream to the mussel stock and simmer to concentrate the flavour and thicken the liquid. You could thicken the stock with a little cornflour dissolved in water if you like.

4 Meanwhile, melt the rest of the butter in a frying pan. Fry the mushrooms, in two batches if necessary. Season with plenty of pepper.

5 Mix the mushrooms, shelled mussels, rocket and tarragon into the sauce. Taste and season with salt if necessary. Sprinkle with chives and capers and serve at once.

PER SERVING GLYCAEMIC LOAD 0; PROTEIN 31 G; CARBOHYDRATES 9 G; FAT 17 G (OF WHICH SATURATES 9 G); FIBRE 3 G

Baked prawns with tomatoes and feta

SERVES 4

24 large raw prawns
4 tablespoons olive oil
200 g (7 oz) shallots, finely sliced
4 garlic cloves, crushed
3 tablespoons fresh thyme leaves
or 1½ tablespoons dried thyme
2 bay leaves
1 cinnamon stick or ½ teaspoon
ground cinnamon
800 g (1¾ lb) ripe tomatoes,
skinned, deseeded and chopped
salt and pepper
250 g (9 oz) feta cheese, crumbled
1 bunch of spring
onions, finely shredded
½ teaspoon aniseed
2 teaspoon cold-pressed flaxseed
oil (optional)

In Greece – where this dish is called saganáki *– the prawns would be cooked in their shells (which keeps them tender and juicy) and served warm rather than finger-burning hot. But if you don't want to eat the prawns with your fingers, peel them before you cook them, leaving the tails on if you like.*

1 Preheat the oven to 180°C/350°F/gas 4. Wash the prawns and pat dry.

2 Heat 2 tablespoons olive oil in a sauté pan over low heat, add the shallots and cook for 5 minutes or until soft. Add 1 crushed garlic clove, together with two-thirds of the thyme, the bay leaves and cinnamon. Add the tomatoes, stir briefly, then cover and simmer for 5–10 minutes, to allow the flavours to blend. Season to taste.

3 Transfer the tomato sauce to a large, shallow ovenproof dish. Sprinkle over the crumbled feta cheese and place in the oven for about 5 minutes.

4 Meanwhile, heat 1 tablespoon oil in a large frying pan. Add the spring onions, the remaining garlic and thyme, and sauté for 1–2 minutes. Add the prawns and aniseed and cook, turning frequently, for a couple of minutes. As soon as the prawns are opaque, add them to the dish with the tomatoes and feta and cook in the oven for a further 10 minutes so the flavours can develop fully.

5 Drizzle the remaining tablespoon of olive oil over the top, together with the flaxseed oil, if using. Leave to cool slightly before serving.

PER SERVING GLYCAEMIC LOAD 0; PROTEIN 23 G; CARBOHYDRATES 12 G; FAT 26 G (OF WHICH SATURATES 10 G); FIBRE 3 G

Marinated prawns

SERVES 4

about 500 g (1 lb 2 oz) peeled
cooked prawns or crayfish tails

MARINADE

100 ml (3½ fl oz) olive oil
½ red chilli, deseeded
and finely chopped
1 tablespoon chopped
fresh coriander
½ red onion, finely chopped
3 garlic cloves, finely chopped
8 black olives,
stoned and chopped
juice of 1 lime
salt and pepper

This dish can be eaten with a slice of good bread (see page 40) for breakfast or brunch, in a salad for lunch or as a first course for dinner. It's a good alternative to a prawn cocktail.

1 Mix together all the ingredients for the marinade. Add the prawns or crayfish tails and stir well. Cover and chill for at least 1 hour.

2 Serve in a glass bowl or on plates with green salad leaves.

PER SERVING GLYCAEMIC LOAD 0; PROTEIN 29 G; CARBOHYDRATES 2 G; FAT 25 G (OF WHICH SATURATES 4 G); FIBRE 0.5 G

 MAKE AHEAD If you wish, you can marinate the prawns up to a day ahead.

Salmon fishcakes

SERVES 4

500 g (1 lb 2 oz) salmon fillet
200 ml (7 fl oz) single cream
45 g (1½ oz) smoked salmon,
finely chopped
1 shallot, finely chopped
1 tablespoon chopped fresh dill
1 egg
salt and pepper
15 g (½ oz) clarified butter
for frying

Instead of salmon, you could use a less expensive white fish. Serve the fishcakes with salad, or with green lentils or mung bean and tomato salad (page 142).

1 Remove the skin from the salmon and run your fingers over the flesh to check there are no bones; if you find any, use tweezers to pull them out. Put the salmon in a food processor and blend briefly.

2 Add the cream, smoked salmon, shallot, dill and egg to the food processor and process at full speed for 10–15 seconds, until you have an even, relatively coarse paste that holds together. Season with salt and pepper.

3 Melt the butter in a non-stick frying pan. Divide the salmon mixture into 8 and shape into cakes. Fry until golden on both sides, turning carefully. If you like, you can finish cooking the fishcakes in the oven at its lowest setting.

PER SERVING GLYCAEMIC LOAD 0; PROTEIN 28 G; CARBOHYDRATES 2.5 G; FAT 29 G (OF WHICH SATURATES 11 G); FIBRE 0 G

MAKE AHEAD The fishcakes can be prepared a day ahead and kept in the refrigerator before cooking. Alternatively, make double quantities, cook all the fishcakes and freeze what you don't use.

Seared salmon with spicy pasta

SERVES 4

400 g (14 oz) skinless, boneless salmon fillet

salt and pepper

2 tablespoons clarified butter

1 onion, finely chopped

1 garlic clove, finely chopped

1 red chilli, seeded and finely chopped

4 tomatoes, diced

1 teaspoon chilli powder

200 ml (7 fl oz) single cream

200 g (7 oz) dried fusilli (preferably wholewheat)

1 tablespoon chopped fresh basil

2 tablespoons chopped flat-leaf parsley

1 tablespoon cold-pressed flaxseed oil (optional)

A salad or some steamed vegetables on the side will make the meal complete.

1 Preheat the oven to 120°C/250°F/gas ½ or the lowest setting.

2 Place the salmon fillet in an ovenproof dish or a small roasting tin. Grind over a little pepper. If you have a roasting thermometer, place it in the thickest part of the fish. Place the salmon in the oven and cook for 25–30 minutes. The core temperature should be 58°C.

3 While the fish is in the oven, melt half the butter in a saucepan over a medium heat. Add the onion, garlic and chilli and cook for 5 minutes or until the vegetables are soft. Add the tomatoes and cook for a further 2 minutes. Add the chilli powder and then the cream. Cook over a low heat for 5 minutes.

4 Meanwhile, boil the pasta in plenty of lightly salted water until al dente. Drain the pasta in a colander.

5 Add the pasta, basil and parsley to the tomato mixture, mix well and heat through. Season with salt and a little more pepper, to taste. Add the flaxseed oil, if using. Serve the salmon with the spicy pasta.

PER SERVING GLYCAEMIC LOAD 14; PROTEIN 26 G; CARBOHYDRATES 44 G; FAT 34 G (OF WHICH SATURATES 14 G); FIBRE 3 G

Lemon-marinated sardines

SERVES 4

1 kg (2¼ lb) fresh sardines, cleaned and filleted

salt and white pepper

2 tablespoons chopped fresh coriander

150 ml (5 fl oz) olive oil

juice of 4 lemons

In this dish, the sardines are 'cooked' by the action of the lemon juice. To make life easier, ask your fishmonger to fillet the sardines for you.

1 Rinse the sardine fillets and dry on kitchen paper. Place in a glass dish, sprinkle with salt, then cover the dish and leave in the refrigerator for 24 hours.

2 Rinse the fillets to remove excess salt and dry thoroughly. Lay the fish in an earthenware dish and sprinkle over the pepper and coriander, then pour over the olive oil and lemon juice. Cover and leave in the refrigerator for 24–48 hours before serving.

PER SERVING GLYCAEMIC LOAD 0; PROTEIN 42 G; CARBOHYDRATES 1 G; FAT 80 G (OF WHICH SATURATES 18 G); FIBRE 0 G

 MAKE AHEAD These sardines need to be prepared at least 48 hours before being served.

Grilled sardines ▶

SERVES 4

1 kg (2¼ lb) fresh sardines, cleaned and scaled

6 tablespoons olive oil

juice of 2 large lemons

1½ tablespoons dried oregano

1 or 2 lemons, quartered, to garnish

This recipe is just as good with other fish – sea bream, small sea bass or red mullet. A fish weighing about 300–350 g (10–12 oz) will serve one person. Greek salad (page 82) would be a good accompaniment, along with delicious almond and garlic sauce (page 104).

1 Wash the fish and pat dry with kitchen paper. Cut 3 shallow slits on each side. Heat the grill or barbecue until very hot and oil the grill rack.

2 Mix the olive oil, lemon juice and oregano. Brush each fish generously inside and out with the herbed oil and lemon mixture.

3 Grill for 3–4 minutes on each side, until the fish is just cooked, basting with more herbed oil as you go.

4 Serve immediately, with the lemon quarters.

PER SERVING GLYCAEMIC LOAD 0; PROTEIN 26 G; CARBOHYDRATES 0 G; FAT 27 G (OF WHICH SATURATES 6 G); FIBRE 0 G

Baked mackerel with tomatoes and garlic

4 medium-sized mackerel, cleaned and rinsed

10 g (⅓ oz) clarified butter for frying

75 ml (3½ fl oz) olive oil

1 onion, finely chopped

3 garlic cloves, finely chopped

4 sun-ripened tomatoes, finely chopped

2 tablespoons chopped parsley

1 tablespoon fructose

salt and pepper

Frozen mackerel fillets also work well and make it even easier to prepare this traditional Greek dish.

1 Preheat the oven to 140°C/275°F/gas 1. Rinse the fish and pat dry.

2 Melt the butter in a frying pan and brown the fish on both sides.

3 Heat the olive oil in a saucepan and add the onion and garlic. Cook over medium heat until the onion is translucent. Add the tomatoes, parsley and fructose. Cook the mixture for 3–4 minutes and season with salt and pepper.

4 Place the mackerel in an ovenproof dish and pour over the tomato sauce. Bake for around 40 minutes; turn the fish over a couple of times or spoon over some of the sauce during the cooking period. The fish is done when the flesh flakes easily when pressed with a fork. Serve hot.

PER SERVING GLYCAEMIC LOAD 0; PROTEIN 39 G; CARBOHYDRATES 9 G; FAT 39 G (OF WHICH SATURATES 8 G); FIBRE 1.5 G

Swordfish with walnut and garlic sauce

4 swordfish steaks (each about 170 g/6 oz)

15 g (½ oz) clarified butter for frying

WALNUT AND GARLIC SAUCE

60 g (2 oz) shelled walnuts

1–2 garlic cloves, crushed

75 g (2½ oz) Parmesan, grated

5 tablespoons chopped flat-leaf parsley or coriander

salt and pepper

2 tablespoons olive oil

½ tablespoon fresh lemon juice

2 tablespoons milk

This is good served with steamed green beans or with pulses such as green lentils, chickpeas or butter beans.

1 Use a food processor or pestle and mortar to make the sauce. Process or grind together the nuts and garlic until very fine and slightly oily. This will take around 1 minute in a food processor or 6 minutes with a pestle and mortar.

2 Add the Parmesan, parsley or coriander and a little pepper. Process or grind until it forms an even paste. Gradually add the olive oil, lemon juice and milk. Season with more salt and pepper to taste.

3 Melt the butter in a frying pan and fry the swordfish steaks on both sides, until just cooked through; do not overcook or the fish will become tough and dry. Serve at once on warmed plates, with a good spoonful of the sauce on each piece of fish.

PER SERVING GLYCAEMIC LOAD 0; PROTEIN 17 G; CARBOHYDRATES 1 G; FAT 26 G (OF WHICH SATURATES 8 G); FIBRE 0.5 G

Red snapper with chickpeas, tomatoes and basil

SERVES 4

4 red snapper fillets, about 300–350 g (10–12 oz) each

3 tablespoons olive oil

3 shallots, chopped

2 x 400 g (14 oz) cans chickpeas, rinsed and drained

2 x 400 g (14 oz) cans chopped tomatoes

2 teaspoons tomato purée (paste)

1 teaspoon balsamic vinegar

1 tablespoon chopped fresh thyme

½ teaspoon fructose

salt and pepper

3 tablespoons chopped fresh basil

2 tablespoons chopped fresh parsley

There's nothing quite like the wonderful aromas of fresh basil and thyme. This recipe will work with other fish, too

1 Rinse the fish fillets and dry them well with kitchen paper. Check that there are no little bones remaining; if you find any, pull them out with tweezers.

2 Heat 2 tablespoons olive oil in a flameproof casserole or large saucepan, add the shallots and chickpeas, and fry for 2–3 minutes. Add the tomatoes with their juice, and the tomato purée. Bring to the boil, then reduce the heat and simmer for 5 minutes.

3 Stir in the balsamic vinegar, thyme and fructose, and season with salt and pepper. Simmer gently for a further 4–5 minutes.

4 Meanwhile, heat a non-stick frying pan, add the remaining olive oil, then add the fish and cook over a moderate heat, turning carefully to cook on both sides.

5 Stir the basil into the tomato mixture, then divide the mixture between 4 warmed soup plates. Place the fish on top, sprinkle with the parsley and serve hot.

PER SERVING GLYCAEMIC LOAD 8; PROTEIN 67 G; CARBOHYDRATES 32 G; FAT 22 G (OF WHICH SATURATES 3 G); FIBRE 8 G

Red mullet with orange, ginger and coriander sauce

SERVES 4

8 small or 4 large red mullet fillets
240 ml (8 fl oz) fresh orange juice
120 ml (4 fl oz) olive oil
1 teaspoon grated fresh ginger
1 teaspoon ground cumin
4–5 tablespoons finely chopped
fresh coriander leaves
salt and pepper
a little clarified butter or
olive oil, for frying

Serve red mullet skin-side up to appreciate its lovely rich colour. Steamed green beans, courgettes (zucchini) or fennel provide a contrast in colour and texture.

1 Run your fingers over the fish fillets to check that no scales or bones remain; if you find any bones, pull them out with tweezers.

2 In a large glass dish, mix together the orange juice, olive oil, ginger, cumin and 2–3 tablespoons of the coriander, reserving some to garnish. Season with salt and pepper. Add the fish and leave in the refrigerator to marinate for 2 hours.

3 Heat a non-stick frying pan, add a little butter or olive oil, then take the fish out of the marinade and cook over a moderate heat, turning carefully to cook on both sides.

4 Transfer the fish to a warmed plate and wipe the pan clean with kitchen paper. Pour the marinade into the pan and cook until it begins to thicken. Serve the fish with the sauce poured around it; sprinkle with chopped coriander.

PER SERVING GLYCAEMIC LOAD 0; PROTEIN 15 G; CARBOHYDRATES 2 G; FAT 23 G (OF WHICH SATURATES 4 G); FIBRE 0 G

Hake with red and green peppers

SERVES 4

800 g (1¾ lb) hake fillet
50 g (1¾ oz) Parmesan, finely grated

TOPPING

4 tablespoons chopped parsley
4 tablespoons olive oil
2 garlic cloves
1 fresh red chilli, deseeded and finely chopped
½ red pepper (capsicum), finely chopped
½ green pepper (capsicum), finely chopped
2 red tomatoes, skinned and diced
1 teaspoon fructose
1 tablespoon balsamic vinegar
salt and pepper

Almost any kind of fish could be used for this recipe. Tzatziki (see page 87) is a good accompaniment or serve with a simple vegetable dish, plus a dish of beans, lentils or chickpeas.

1 Preheat the oven to 120°C/250°F/gas ½ or the lowest setting. Mix together the ingredients for the topping.

2 Cut the fish into 4 portions and place in an ovenproof dish or roasting tin. Spread the topping over the fish and sprinkle Parmesan on top. Bake for 30 minutes. Serve hot.

PER SERVING GLYCAEMIC LOAD 0; PROTEIN 40 G; CARBOHYDRATES 4 G; FAT 17 G (OF WHICH SATURATES 4 G); FIBRE 1 G

Cod with pesto

SERVES 4

800 g (1¾ lb) cod fillet
4 tablespoons pesto sauce, ready-made or see page 86
black pepper

You could use almost any filleted fish in this simple, tasty recipe: try it with sea bass, tuna, plaice or other flat fish. Cooking at low temperatures keeps the fish moist and tender.

1 Preheat the oven to 120°C/250°F/gas ½ or the lowest setting. Remove the skin from the fish and run your fingers over the flesh to check that there are no bones; if you find any, pull them out with tweezers.

2 Put the fish in a lightly oiled roasting tin in one layer. Spread pesto over the fish and sprinkle with black pepper. Stick a cooking thermometer, preferably digital, into the thickest part of the fish and set the thermometer to 58°C (no need to do this with thin fillets of fish). Bake for about 30 minutes or until the fish is cooked through. Serve hot.

PER SERVING GLYCAEMIC LOAD 0; PROTEIN 35 G; CARBOHYDRATES 0 G; FAT 15 G (OF WHICH SATURATES 2.5 G); FIBRE 0 G

Monkfish with herbed olive oil

SERVES 4

800 g (1¾ lb) monkfish fillet

100 ml (3½ fl oz) olive oil

4 tablespoons chopped fresh herbs (e.g. basil, thyme, flat-leaf parsley)

2 tablespoons freshly grated Parmesan

1 tablespoon lemon juice

salt and pepper

This works just as well with flat fish such as sole or flounder, or with less expensive fish such as coley.

1 Preheat the oven to 120°C/250°F/gas ½ or its lowest setting.

2 Place the oil, herbs, Parmesan, lemon juice, salt and pepper in a measuring jug and, using a hand-held blender, process the mixture until it is fairly smooth, green and viscous.

3 Cut the fish into 4 portions. Place the fish in an ovenproof dish or roasting tin. Spoon the herbed oil over the fish to coat well. Note – you may not need all the oil: it can be served as a sauce on the side or reserved for another use. Store in an airtight jar in the refrigerator.

4 Place the fish in the oven. Ideally, use a digital roasting thermometer and place it in the thickest part of one of the pieces of fish (no need to do this with thin fillets of fish). The fish is done when the thermometer reads 60°C. The cooking time will be about 30 minutes, but this will vary slightly depending on the thickness of the fish. Serve hot.

PER SERVING GLYCAEMIC LOAD 0; PROTEIN 38 G; CARBOHYDRATES 0 G; FAT 30 G (OF WHICH SATURATES 5 G); FIBRE 0 G

Grilled chicken with almond and garlic sauce

SERVES 4

2 spring chickens (poussins), about 850 g (approx. 2 lb) each

juice of 1 lemon

3 tablespoons olive oil

½ tablespoon dried oregano

3 tablespoons dry white wine

2 garlic cloves, finely chopped

1 onion, finely chopped

salt and pepper

2 tablespoons chopped fresh herbs (e.g. parsley, thyme, oregano)

lemon wedges, to serve

ALMOND AND GARLIC SAUCE

250 g (9 oz) dried large white beans, such as butter beans

50 g (1¾ oz) ground almonds

2 garlic cloves

1 tablespoon white wine vinegar

100 ml (3½ fl oz) olive oil

1 tablespoon fresh lemon juice

1 teaspoon cold-pressed flaxseed oil

½ teaspoon sea salt

½ teaspoon ground white pepper

For the best flavour, marinate the chicken overnight. If you're short of time, use a 425 g (15 oz) can of cannellini or butter beans instead of the dried beans. With this rich, garlicky sauce, you only need a fresh salad to complete the meal.

1 For the sauce, soak the beans for at least 8 hours, or overnight, in water to cover.

2 Cut each chicken along the backbone and remove as much of the backbone as possible. Press each chicken with your fist to flatten slightly, then place them in a large glass dish that will fit in the refrigerator.

3 Combine the lemon juice, olive oil, oregano, wine, garlic, onion and some salt and pepper in a blender (or use a hand-held blender) and blend together to make a paste. Spread the paste over the chicken and massage it into the meat. Cover the dish and put into the refrigerator to marinate, preferably overnight.

4 The next day, drain the beans, put them in a saucepan and add enough fresh water to come 7–8 cm (3 in) above the beans. Bring to the boil and boil for 10 minutes, then reduce the heat and simmer the beans for 1–1½ hours or until completely soft. Drain well.

5 Put the cooked beans, almonds, garlic and vinegar in a food processor and process to a smooth paste. Reduce the speed and gradually add the olive oil and lemon juice through the hole in the lid, processing to a thick sauce. Add the flaxseed oil and season with the salt and pepper. Set aside.

6 Preheat the grill to high, prepare a barbecue or preheat the oven to 180°C/350°F/gas 4. Wipe away excess marinade from the chicken, then cook under the hot grill, on the barbecue or in a roasting tin in the oven until cooked through. Test by piercing the thickest part of the flesh with a thin skewer: when the chicken is cooked the juices should run clear. Sprinkle the grilled chicken with chopped herbs and serve with the almond and garlic sauce and lemon wedges.

PER SERVING GLYCAEMIC LOAD 0; PROTEIN 40 G; CARBOHYDRATES 0 G; FAT 24 G (OF WHICH SATURATES 4 G); FIBRE 0 G

 MAKE AHEAD The sauce can be made up to 3 days ahead; store in the refrigerator. Serve cool or at room temperature.

Spanish chicken casserole with green lentils

Ole! A delicious casserole with heart-healthy oils and the wonderful scent of cumin.

SERVES 4

200 g (7 oz) green lentils

1 tablespoon olive oil

15 g (½ oz) clarified butter

4 skinless, boneless chicken breasts, cut into 2 cm (¾ in) cubes

1 small onion, finely chopped

1 green pepper (capsicum), deseeded and diced

2 sticks of celery, finely diced

400 g (14 oz) can chopped tomatoes

400 ml (14 fl oz) chicken stock

2 garlic cloves, crushed

1 teaspoon ground cumin

pinch of cayenne pepper, or to taste

salt and pepper

1 tablespoon cold-pressed flaxseed oil

2 tablespoons chopped fresh flat-leaf parsley

1 Put the lentils in a saucepan, cover with plenty of water and simmer until soft. When the lentils are cooked, drain off any excess water, then mix with the olive oil and keep hot.

2 Meanwhile, melt the butter in a large saucepan over moderate heat. Add the chicken and fry for about 4 minutes, turning the pieces so they colour evenly. Transfer to a plate.

3 Lower the heat slightly and add the onion, green pepper and celery to the pan. Cook for 4 minutes or until the vegetables start to soften. Stir in the tomatoes and stock. Simmer gently for 10–12 minutes.

4 Add the garlic, cumin and cayenne pepper to the tomato sauce. Season with salt and pepper, if necessary. Return the chicken to the sauce and simmer for 10–15 minutes, until cooked through.

5 Place the hot lentils in a serving dish and gently mix in the chicken and sauce. Sprinkle with the flaxseed oil and parsley and serve hot.

PER SERVING GLYCAEMIC LOAD 2; PROTEIN 66 G; CARBOHYDRATES 8 G; FAT 33 G (OF WHICH SATURATES 6 G); FIBRE 3 G

Chicken baked in spiced yogurt

SERVES 4

6 skinless chicken legs or
6 thighs and 6 drumsticks
115 g (4 oz) natural yogurt
120 ml (4 fl oz) olive oil
juice of 1 lemon
2 garlic cloves, crushed
1 teaspoon paprika
good pinch of ground cinnamon
pinch of cayenne pepper
salt and pepper
15 g (½ oz) clarified butter
lemon wedges, to serve

These chicken legs make an easy supper dish, but are just as good cold for a summer lunch. Serve with a bean or lentil dish and a mixed salad.

1 Dry the chicken well with kitchen paper. If using legs, divide each leg into thighs and drumsticks by cutting just above the knee joint.

2 Mix together the yogurt, olive oil, lemon juice, garlic, paprika, cinnamon, cayenne pepper and some salt and pepper in a resealable plastic bag. Add the chicken pieces and seal the bag. Squeeze the bag gently to distribute the marinade all over the chicken. Leave in the refrigerator for at least 2–3 hours or, preferably, overnight.

3 Preheat the oven to 120°C/250°F/gas ½ or the lowest setting. Melt the butter in a frying pan, add the chicken and marinade and brown the chicken pieces on all sides. Transfer them to a roasting tin and finish cooking in the oven for about 40–50 minutes. If you are using a roasting thermometer, insert into the thickest part of a thigh and set the temperature to 66°C.

4 Serve the chicken hot or cold, with lemon wedges.

PER SERVING GLYCAEMIC LOAD 0; PROTEIN 26 G; CARBOHYDRATES 4 G; FAT 13 G (OF WHICH SATURATES 3 G); FIBRE 0.5 G

MAKE AHEAD The chicken is best prepared a day in advance and left to marinate. If you want to serve it cold, it can be cooked a day or two ahead and stored in the refrigerator.

Greek chicken with artichokes and avgolemono

SERVES 4

1 chicken, about 1.5 kg (3 lb 5 oz), skinned and cut into 4 or 8 portions

salt and pepper

3 tablespoons olive oil

1 large red onion, finely chopped

2 garlic cloves, finely chopped

1 tablespoon tomato purée (paste)

juice of 1 lemon

200 ml (7 fl oz) brandy or dry white wine

1 teaspoon ground cinnamon

4 fresh, frozen (defrosted) or canned (rinsed) artichoke bottoms

50 g (1¾ oz) pine nuts, toasted in a non-stick pan

AVGOLEMONO

2 eggs

juice of 2 lemons

Avgolemono is a classic Greek sauce: the name means 'egg and lemon'. Serve the chicken with a simple bean or lentil dish, such as yellow split pea purée (page 138) or with couscous or brown rice if this is your reward meal.

1 Season the chicken with salt and pepper. Heat 2 tablespoons olive oil in a sauté pan and brown the chicken on all sides. Remove the chicken from the pan and pour off the fat.

2 Add the remaining olive oil to the pan, then add the onion and garlic and cook until the onion begins to colour. Add the tomato purée and mix well, then add the lemon juice.

3 Return the chicken to the pan, add the brandy or wine and sprinkle with cinnamon, salt and pepper. Add enough water to half-cover the chicken, then cover with a lid and leave to simmer for 25 minutes.

4 Add the artichokes to the pan and top up the water if necessary: the artichokes should be almost submerged. Cover and simmer gently for a further 25–30 minutes, or until the chicken and artichokes are quite tender.

5 Just before serving, make the avgolemono sauce: whisk together the eggs and lemon juice until they are pale and light. Gradually whisk in a ladleful of the hot chicken cooking liquid, stirring constantly. Pour the mixture over and around the chicken and stir well, then remove the pan from the heat and continue stirring for about 3 minutes, until the sauce thickens. Do not let the sauce boil or the eggs will curdle. Serve hot, sprinkled with toasted pine nuts.

PER SERVING GLYCAEMIC LOAD 0; PROTEIN 27 G; CARBOHYDRATES 3 G; FAT 37 G (OF WHICH SATURATES 8 G); FIBRE 0 G

Chicken kebabs with fresh herbs

SERVES 4

750 g (1 lb 10 oz) skinless
chicken breast, cut
into 2.5 cm (1 in) chunks

4 tablespoons olive oil

4 garlic cloves, crushed

1 teaspoon dried mint

1 teaspoon dried oregano

pinch of salt

1 teaspoon pepper

2 tablespoons fresh lemon juice

1 bunch fresh mint

1 aubergine (eggplant), cut into
2.5 cm (1 in) chunks

1 red onion, cut into wedges

1 red or yellow pepper (capsicum),
cut into 2.5 cm (1 in) chunks

1 lemon, cut into 8 chunks

The taste of the Mediterranean: aromatic grilled chicken with vegetables and herbs. Serve with a Greek salad (page 82).

1 Mix the chicken, 2 tablespoons olive oil, garlic, dried herbs, salt and pepper in a bowl and leave to marinate for 30 minutes.

2 Whisk the remaining olive oil with the lemon juice. Preheat the grill until very hot.

3 Remove the mint leaves from their stems. Thread the chicken, mint leaves, aubergine, onion and pepper onto 8 metal skewers, with a chunk of lemon at the end. Sprinkle with salt and pepper and brush with the oil and lemon mixture. Cook for about 9 minutes, turning and basting with the oil and lemon mixture, until the chicken is just cooked through. Serve at once, with salad.

PER SERVING GLYCAEMIC LOAD 2; PROTEIN 100 G; CARBOHYDRATES 35 G; FAT 60 G (OF WHICH SATURATES 14 G); FIBRE 8 G

MAKE AHEAD The chicken can be marinated up to 8 hours in advance. The kebabs can be prepared up to 2 hours ahead and stored in the refrigerator.

Chicken with chilli and lemon thyme

SERVES 4

15 g (½ oz) clarified butter
4 skinless, boneless chicken
breasts, 150–180 g (5½–6 oz) each
2 tablespoons sweet
Thai chilli sauce
1 tablespoon finely chopped
fresh lemon thyme
salt

If you can't obtain lemon thyme, try this with basil instead. Serve with stir-fried vegetables such as mangetouts, red or yellow peppers (capsicums) or bean sprouts.

1 Preheat the oven to 120°C/250°F/gas ½ or the lowest setting.

2 Heat a heavy, non-stick frying pan over moderate heat, add the butter and brown the chicken breasts on both sides. Transfer them to a small roasting tin or ovenproof dish.

3 Mix the chilli sauce with the thyme. Brush over the chicken breasts (do not use more than necessary since chilli sauce can be very sweet) and sprinkle with a little salt. If you have a digital roasting thermometer, insert it into the thickest part of one of the chicken breasts and set it to 65°C. Place the chicken in the oven and roast for about 30 minutes, or until cooked through. Serve hot.

PER SERVING GLYCAEMIC LOAD 0; PROTEIN 35 G; CARBOHYDRATES 1 G; FAT 8 G (OF WHICH SATURATES 4 G); FIBRE 0 G

Parmesan-coated chicken breasts

SERVES 4

clarified butter for frying
4 skinless, boneless
chicken breasts
50 g (1¾ oz) fresh
Parmesan, finely grated
black pepper

Say 'cheese' and smile, for this easy dish tastes fantastic.

1 Preheat the oven to 160°C/325°F/gas 3. Put a little clarified butter in a heavy frying pan, preferably non-stick, and let the butter brown slightly. Then add the chicken breasts and brown them quickly on both sides. Remove from the heat and leave to cool slightly.

2 Spread the Parmesan on a plate and season with pepper. Turn the chicken breasts in the Parmesan to coat all over, then arrange them in an ovenproof dish or roasting tin.

3 Place in the oven and bake for about 10 minutes or until cooked through. If using a roasting thermometer, set the temperature to 65°C. Serve hot.

PER SERVING GLYCAEMIC LOAD 0; PROTEIN 40 G; CARBOHYDRATES 7 G; FAT 23 G (OF WHICH SATURATES 8 G); FIBRE 1.5 G

Chicken with shallots and cinnamon

SERVES 4

25 g (scant 1 oz) clarified butter

6 skinless chicken legs, divided into thighs and drumsticks

400 g (14 oz) small shallots, peeled

300 ml (10 fl oz) chicken stock

1 teaspoon ground cinnamon

1 teaspoon fructose

½ teaspoon finely chopped fresh rosemary

salt and pepper

50 g (1¾ oz) pine nuts, lightly toasted in a dry frying pan

1 tablespoon olive oil

Serve with steamed vegetables such as green beans, courgettes (zucchini), leeks or carrots and spoon the aromatic cooking liquid over the chicken and vegetables.

1 Melt half the butter in a flameproof casserole and brown the chicken pieces quickly on all sides. Remove the chicken from the pot and set aside. Wipe out the pot with kitchen paper.

2 Melt the rest of the butter in the casserole and add the shallots. Fry over low heat until softened and slightly coloured but not brown.

3 Return the chicken pieces to the casserole, then pour in the stock. Add the cinnamon, fructose and rosemary, and season with salt and pepper. Bring to the boil, then reduce the heat and simmer for about 40 minutes or until the chicken meat is falling off the bone.

4 Serve hot, sprinkling each serving with toasted pine nuts and a few drops of olive oil.

PER SERVING GLYCAEMIC LOAD 0; PROTEIN 31 G; CARBOHYDRATES 0 G; FAT 12 G (OF WHICH SATURATES 6 G); FIBRE 0 G

MAKE AHEAD Cook the chicken up to 2 days in advance and store in the refrigerator; reheat thoroughly. Make double quantities and freeze half.

◄ Chicken with tomatoes and ouzo

SERVES 4

3 tablespoons olive oil
1 chicken, about 1.5 kg
(3 lb 5 oz), cut into 8 pieces
salt and pepper
6 garlic cloves, chopped
1½ teaspoons aniseeds, crushed,
or ground star anise
2 x 400 g (14 oz) cans
plum tomatoes
120 ml (4 fl oz) chicken stock
80 ml (3 fl oz) ouzo (or stock)
1 tablespoon dried oregano
12 black olives, stoned
125 g (4½ oz) feta
cheese, crumbled

*If you haven't got a bottle of ouzo left over from a Greek holiday,
use Pernod or Ricard.*

1 Heat the oil in a large sauté pan over medium heat. Add the
chicken, season and brown thoroughly on all sides.

2 Pour off all but 2 tablespoons of fat from the pan. Add the garlic
and aniseed and stir for 30 seconds. Add the tomatoes, stock, ouzo
and oregano. Bring to the boil, crushing the tomatoes with the back
of a spoon. Return the chicken to the pan, bring to the boil, then
simmer, uncovered, for 15 minutes. Turn the chicken and simmer for a
further 5 minutes. Remove the chicken from the sauce and keep warm.

3 Add the olives to the sauce and boil for 6–8 minutes, until it
thickens, stirring frequently. Season to taste. Serve the chicken on
warmed plates, spoon the sauce over, sprinkle over the feta cheese
and serve immediately.

PER SERVING GLYCAEMIC LOAD 1; PROTEIN 40 G; CARBOHYDRATES 30 G; FAT 10 G
(OF WHICH SATURATES 2 G); FIBRE 6 G

 MAKE AHEAD This recipe can be made a day in advance, but add
the feta just before serving.

Spicy lemon chicken

SERVES 4

grated zest and juice of 2 lemons
4 garlic cloves, finely chopped
1 large onion, finely chopped
1 teaspoon sambal oelek
(Indonesian chilli sauce)
2 tablespoons olive oil
salt and pepper
6 skinless chicken legs or other
skinless chicken pieces
4 tablespoons chopped
fresh flat-leaf parsley

*Serve with cucumber or carrot salad or hot vegetables, as well as
a dish of lentils or beans.*

1 Mix together the lemon zest and juice, garlic, onion, sambal oelek,
olive oil and some salt and pepper. Place the chicken and lemon mixture
in a resealable plastic bag and seal well. Leave the chicken to marinate
in the refrigerator overnight.

2 Preheat the oven to 120°C/250°F/gas ½ or the lowest setting. Take the
chicken out of the marinade and place in a roasting tin. Roast for about
1 hour or until cooked through. If are using a roasting thermometer, set
the temperature to 66°C for legs or 65°C for breasts. Serve hot,
sprinkled with chopped parsley.

PER SERVING GLYCAEMIC LOAD 0; PROTEIN 29 G; CARBOHYDRATES 10 G; FAT 24 G
(OF WHICH SATURATES 7 G); FIBRE 1.5 G

Slow-roast turkey breast with herbed olive oil

SERVES 4

100 ml (3½ fl oz) olive oil

4 tablespoons chopped fresh herbs (e.g. basil, thyme, flat-leaf parsley)

1 boneless turkey breast joint, about 700 g (1½ lb)

salt and pepper

Serve this aromatic roast with roasted mixed vegetables (page 126) or a tomato salad.

1 Preheat the oven to 120°C/250°F/gas ½ or the lowest setting. Place the oil and herbs in a blender (or use a hand-held blender) and blend until smooth, green and thick.

2 Dry the turkey with kitchen paper and place it in a roasting tin. Using a spoon or brush, coat the breast generously with herbed oil and season with a little salt and pepper (note that you may not need all the oil: store the remainder in a jar in the refrigerator and serve as a sauce, or stir into a lentil or bean dish). If you have a roasting thermometer, insert it into the thickest part of the joint and set the thermometer to 65°C.

3 Place the turkey in the oven. The roasting time will vary depending on the thickness of the breast, but it will be about 1½ hours. If the turkey breast is cooked before you are ready to serve it, open the oven door, but leave the turkey in the oven.

PER SERVING GLYCAEMIC LOAD 0; PROTEIN 42 G; CARBOHYDRATES 7 G; FAT 17 G (OF WHICH SATURATES 3.5 G); FIBRE 2 G

 MAKE AHEAD The herbed oil can be made up to 3 days in advance; store in a jar in the refrigerator and stir well before using.

Garlic and rosemary-scented turkey

SERVES 4

1 boneless turkey breast joint,
about 700 g (1 ½ lb)
15 g (½ oz) clarified butter

GARLIC AND ROSEMARY PASTE
2 garlic bulbs
30 g (1 oz) butter, melted
2 tablespoons olive oil
1 tablespoon finely
chopped fresh rosemary
1 tablespoon Dijon mustard
½ teaspoon salt
½ teaspoon black pepper

I just love the combination of rosemary and mustard, which is great with lamb as well as turkey. You can easily make variations on this recipe by using tarragon, thyme, oregano or basil instead of rosemary.

1 Preheat the oven to 180°C/350°F/gas 4. To make the garlic paste, cut the top 1 cm (½ in) or so off the garlic bulbs – just enough to reveal the cloves. Place the garlic, cut side up, in a small roasting tin. Drizzle the melted butter over the garlic and cover the tin with aluminium foil. Roast for about 1 hour 20 minutes or until the garlic is completely soft but not browned.

2 Take the tin out of the oven, remove the foil and leave the garlic to cool for about 45 minutes. Then press the garlic cloves out of the bulbs one by one and put them in a blender or food processor. Add the olive oil, rosemary, mustard, salt and pepper and process to a very smooth paste. Set aside.

3 Reduce the oven temperature to 120°C/250°F/gas ½ or the lowest setting. Dry the turkey with kitchen paper. Melt the butter in a frying pan and brown the breast quickly on all sides. Transfer to a roasting tin. Spread a generous layer of garlic paste over the breast. Insert a roasting thermometer (ideally digital) into the thickest part of the joint and set the thermometer to 65°C. Place in the oven and roast for about 1½ hours, or until cooked through, depending on the thickness of the breast. Serve hot.

PER SERVING GLYCAEMIC LOAD 0; PROTEIN 40 G; CARBOHYDRATES 0.5 G; FAT 17 G (OF WHICH SATURATES 7 G); FIBRE 0 G

MAKE AHEAD The garlic paste may be made up to 2 days in advance and stored in a jar in the refrigerator. Make double or treble quantities for use in other recipes: on chicken breasts, leg of lamb or lamb cutlets.

Souvlaki with red pepper sauce ▶

SERVES 4

800 g (1¾ lb) lean lamb, trimmed, from the leg
bunch of bay leaves, preferably fresh
1 lemon, cut into wedges, to serve

MARINADE
4 tablespoons olive oil
juice of 1 lemon
2 teaspoons dried or fresh thyme
2 garlic cloves, crushed
black pepper

RED PEPPER SAUCE
6 red peppers (capsicums), halved and deseeded
2 tablespoons olive oil
1 red chilli, deseeded and finely chopped (optional)
6 garlic cloves, finely chopped
2 tablespoons red wine vinegar
1 teaspoon cold-pressed flaxseed oil
2 teaspoons dried oregano or spearmint

This delicious dish tastes even better prepared on a barbecue.

1 Dice the lamb into 2.5 cm (1 in) pieces.

2 Make the marinade: mix the olive oil, lemon juice, thyme, garlic and pepper. Place the meat in a bowl, pour the marinade over and mix well so that all the pieces of meat are coated. Leave in the refrigerator for at least 2 hours, or overnight.

3 Meanwhile, make the sauce. Preheat the oven to 220°C/425°F/gas 7. Place the peppers in a roasting tin, add 1 tablespoon olive oil and mix well with your hands. Roast until the peppers begin to brown. Put the peppers into a plastic bag, seal and leave for about 10 minutes.

4 Peel the peppers and put them into a blender or food processor with the remaining sauce ingredients. Blend until completely smooth. Taste and season with salt and pepper if necessary.

5 Preheat the grill and the oven to 120°C/250°F/gas ½ or the lowest setting. Thread the meat on to 4 skewers, with the bay leaves. Grill the kebabs quickly until browned on all sides. Brush the kebabs with the marinade and finish cooking in the oven, 20–25 minutes. Serve with lemon wedges and the red pepper sauce.

PER SERVING GLYCAEMIC LOAD 0; PROTEIN 44 G; CARBOHYDRATES 16 G; FAT 36 G (OF WHICH SATURATES 11 G); FIBRE 4 G

Lamb meatballs

SERVES 4

250 g (9 oz) minced lamb
250 g (9 oz) minced beef
1 onion, finely chopped
1 tomato, finely diced
2 garlic cloves, finely chopped
½ red pepper (capsicum), finely chopped
1 teaspoon rosemary, preferably fresh, finely chopped
2 eggs
½ red chilli, deseeded and finely chopped
salt and pepper
15 g (½ oz) clarified butter

Serve with tzatziki (page 87) and a bean or lentil dish such as yellow split pea purée (page 138).

1 Preheat the oven to 120°C/250°F/gas ½ or the lowest setting.

2 Mix all the ingredients, except the butter, in a bowl or in a food processor. Fry a walnut-sized piece of the mixture in a non-stick frying pan and taste to decide whether it needs more salt or pepper.

3 Shape the mixture into meatballs. Melt the butter in the frying pan, add the meatballs and brown them, in batches if necessary. Finish cooking the meatballs in a roasting tin in the oven for about 20 minutes, until cooked through (do not overcook or they will become dry).

PER SERVING GLYCAEMIC LOAD 0; PROTEIN 30 G; CARBOHYDRATES 6 G; FAT 14 G (OF WHICH SATURATES 7 G); FIBRE 1.5 G

Lamb with apricots and almonds

SERVES 4

2 tablespoons clarified butter

700 g (1 lb 9 oz) lamb, diced

1 onion, roughly chopped

2 garlic cloves, finely chopped

2 teaspoons ground cumin

3 teaspoons ground coriander

800 ml (28 fl oz) stock

a little grated fresh ginger

2 carrots, cut into large pieces

150 g (5½ oz) green beans, fresh
or frozen

100 g (3½ oz) dried apricots,
roughly chopped

a handful of almonds,
roughly chopped

salt and pepper

This wonderful dish is a fusion of Mediterranean and Indian flavours.

1 Melt 1 tablespoon of the butter in a flameproof casserole, add the lamb and brown lightly. Remove the meat from the pan and set aside.

2 Melt the rest of the butter in the casserole and add the onion, garlic, cumin and coriander. Let it colour slightly. Return the meat to the casserole and add the stock and ginger. Simmer for about 40 minutes.

3 Add the carrots and cook for about 10 minutes. Add the beans and apricots and cook for a further 2–7 minutes, depending on whether the beans are frozen or fresh. Add the almonds and season to taste with salt and pepper. Serve hot.

PER SERVING GLYCAEMIC LOAD 5; PROTEIN 40 G; CARBOHYDRATES 17 G; FAT 27 G (OF WHICH SATURATES 13 G); FIBRE 4 G

MAKE AHEAD Prepare up to the end of step 2 and store in the refrigerator for up to 3 days. It can also be frozen for 2 months.

Fricassée of lamb

This hearty stew is perfect for dinner on a cold winter's evening.

SERVES 4

750 g (1 lb 10 oz) lean lamb

bouquet garni (celery, parsley and thyme, wrapped in a piece of leek and tied with string)

1 litre (1¾ pints) water or stock

3 carrots

1 small celeriac

2 slices swede

100 ml (3½ fl oz) single cream

3 tablespoons cornflour

salt and pepper

2 tablespoons chopped fresh parsley or dill

1 Cut the meat into 4 cm (1½ in) cubes. Place the meat and bouquet garni in a saucepan and add the water or stock. Bring to the boil, then immediately reduce the heat and simmer gently for about 45 minutes to 1 hour, until the meat is tender, skimming the surface occasionally.

2 Meanwhile peel the vegetables and dice them or cut into sticks. Cook in plenty of boiling water until al dente (still with a bit of bite). Drain and refresh the vegetables under cold water.

3 When the meat is tender, remove the bouquet garni and strain the stock into a measuring jug. Transfer the meat to a warmed dish and pour 600 ml (1 pint) of the stock back into the saucepan. Add the cream and bring to the boil. Dissolve the cornflour in a little cold water and stir it into the boiling liquid. Season with salt and pepper.

4 Place the meat and vegetables in the sauce and heat through for a few minutes. Stir in the dill or parsley and serve hot.

PER SERVING GLYCAEMIC LOAD 11; PROTEIN 40 G; CARBOHYDRATES 25 G; FAT 21 G (OF WHICH SATURATES 10 G); FIBRE 2.5 G

Roast lamb with herbs and garlic

The best cut of meat is a boned leg, preferably tunnel-boned – the joint remains in one piece. Tie the joint into shape or ask your butcher to do this. Alternatively, use a half leg of lamb on the bone.

SERVES 4

1 joint of lamb weighing 1–1½ kg (2¼–3¼ lb)

2–3 garlic cloves, cut into slivers

3 tablespoons olive oil

1 tablespoon fresh rosemary, finely chopped

1 tablespoon fresh thyme, finely chopped

2 tablespoons flat-leaf parsley, chopped

salt and pepper

1 Preheat the oven to 120°C/250°F/gas ½ or the lowest setting. Using a small sharp knife, make small pockets in the meat and insert the slivers of garlic.

2 Mix the olive oil, rosemary, thyme and parsley to make a herbed oil – a hand-held blender will do this quickly. Season with salt and pepper.

3 Heat a large roasting tin over medium heat and brown the joint all over, then brush the herbed oil over the meat. If you have one, insert a digital roasting thermometer into the thickest part of the meat and set the temperature to 66°C for pink-cooked meat. If the temperature exceeds 75°C the meat will be grey and dry. Roast for about 2 hours.

PER SERVING GLYCAEMIC LOAD 0; PROTEIN 44 G; CARBOHYDRATES 0 G; FAT 20 G (OF WHICH SATURATES 7 G); FIBRE 0 G

Pork casserole with chickpeas and orange

SERVES 6

300 g (10½ oz) chickpeas, soaked overnight

3 tablespoons clarified butter

700 g (1 lb 9 oz) pork shoulder, cut into 4 cm (1½ in) cubes

2 onions, sliced

2 garlic cloves, finely chopped

½ red chilli, deseeded and finely chopped

400 g (14 oz) can chopped tomatoes

grated zest of 1 orange

salt and pepper

2 tablespoons olive oil

If you are in a hurry, use canned chickpeas for this spicy, orange-scented dish.

1 Drain the chickpeas, rinse them and place in a large saucepan. Add water to a finger's width above the chickpeas. Put on the lid and bring to the boil for 10 minutes. Reduce the heat and simmer gently for an hour or so, until the chickpeas are soft, skimming occasionally. Drain the chickpeas, retaining the cooking water.

2 Melt the butter in a heavy-based saucepan and add the pork. Brown the meat on all sides, then transfer to a plate and set aside.

3 Put the onions in the pan and fry until golden. Add the garlic and chilli and fry for a few seconds. Add the tomatoes and orange zest and bring to the boil.

4 Add the chickpeas and meat to the tomato mixture. Add enough cooking water from the chickpeas to cover. Grind in a little pepper and mix well. Bring to the boil, then reduce the heat and simmer for 1 hour. Stir occasionally and add more water if necessary, to keep the meat and chickpeas moist. Season to taste and serve in warmed soup plates; pour on the olive oil before serving.

PER SERVING GLYCAEMIC LOAD 8; PROTEIN 36 G; CARBOHYDRATES 30 G; FAT 23 G (OF WHICH SATURATES 9 G); FIBRE 6 G

 MAKE AHEAD This dish can be made a day in advance. Alternatively, it can be frozen for up to 2 months.

One-pot casserole with cinnamon

SERVES 4

2 tablespoons clarified butter

500 g (1 lb 2 oz) lean minced beef, ideally less than 10% fat

1 onion, finely chopped

100 g (3½ oz) button mushrooms, sliced

400 g (14 oz) can chopped tomatoes

1 teaspoon dried thyme

½ teaspoon ground cinnamon

2 carrots, cut into chunks

1 small leek, sliced

150 g (5½ oz) red lentils, rinsed

salt and pepper

2 teaspoons fructose (optional)

2 tablespoons olive oil

1 tablespoon chopped fresh parsley, to serve

A straightforward recipe for a hearty casserole.

1 Melt 1 tablespoon of the butter in a frying pan and add the beef and onion. Brown over relatively high heat, breaking up the mince with a wooden spoon. As soon as the meat has lost its redness, transfer to a large saucepan. Melt the rest of the butter in the frying pan and add the mushrooms; brown lightly and add to the saucepan.

2 Add the tomatoes, 300 ml (10 fl oz) water, thyme and cinnamon to the saucepan. Bring to a simmer and cook for about 10 minutes. Add the carrots, leek and lentils and cook for a further 15 minutes, or until the lentils are soft.

3 Season the casserole with salt and pepper, and fructose if you like. Serve hot, sprinkled with olive oil and parsley.

PER SERVING GLYCAEMIC LOAD 7; PROTEIN 37 G; CARBOHYDRATES 33 G; FAT 20 G (OF WHICH SATURATES 9 G); FIBRE 5 G

 MAKE AHEAD This dish can be made up to 5 days in advance or frozen for 2 months.

Ragout of beef with onions

SERVES 4

3 tablespoons clarified butter

700 g (1 lb 9 oz) lean beef, cut into 5 cm (2 in) cubes

200 g (7 oz) can chopped tomatoes

2 tablespoons tomato purée (paste)

400 ml (14 fl oz) water

2 onions, roughly chopped

2 garlic cloves, finely chopped

½ teaspoon cinnamon

1 teaspoon dried thyme

salt and pepper

2 tablespoons olive oil

3 tablespoons chopped flat-leaf parsley

This is a traditional Greek dish called kokkinisto, *meaning red. The combination of onions, garlic, cinnamon and tomatoes is very tasty.*

1 Melt half the butter in a heavy-based saucepan, add the meat and brown on all sides.

2 Add the tomatoes, tomato purée and water. Simmer for 15 minutes.

3 Meanwhile, melt the remaining butter in a frying pan. Add the onions and garlic and fry for a few minutes until golden. Add this to the meat, together with the cinnamon, thyme and a little salt and pepper. Cover and simmer for about 1½ hours, or until the meat is completely tender. Add more water during the cooking period if necessary.

4 Serve hot, sprinkled with olive oil and parsley.

PER SERVING GLYCAEMIC LOAD 0; PROTEIN 37 G; CARBOHYDRATES 9 G; FAT 23 G (OF WHICH SATURATES 10 G); FIBRE 2 G

 MAKE AHEAD This dish can be made up to 5 days in advance or frozen for 2 months.

Stuffed peppers

SERVES 4

4 medium or 8 small peppers (capsicums)

2 tablespoons olive oil

500 g (1 lb 2 oz) lean minced meat (beef, lamb or pork)

1 onion, finely chopped

2 garlic cloves

½ red chilli, deseeded and finely chopped

1 tablespoon dried thyme

2 teaspoons Dijon mustard

1 teaspoon fructose

400 g (14 oz) can chopped tomatoes

3 tablespoons tomato purée (paste)

400 ml (14 fl oz) water

salt and pepper

chopped fresh parsley and oregano, to serve

You could use tomatoes or courgettes (zucchini) instead of the peppers; the cooking time will be slightly shorter.

1 Preheat the oven to 160°C/325°F/gas 3.

2 Wash and dry the peppers. Slice off the tops and reserve. Scrape out the seeds.

3 Heat 1 tablespoon of the oil in a saucepan, add the minced meat, onion, garlic and chilli and stir over the heat until the meat looks crumbly and has lost its redness. Add the thyme, mustard, fructose, tomatoes, tomato purée and water and simmer until the mixture has thickened slightly, about 15 minutes. Remove from the heat and season with salt and pepper.

4 Fill the peppers with the meat mixture; do not overfill. Place the filled peppers in a roasting tin just large enough to hold them snugly. Cover with the reserved tops and brush with olive oil.

5 Bake for 50–60 minutes, until the peppers are tender. You may want to add a little boiling water to the roasting tin during cooking if the vegetables look dry. Serve hot, sprinkled with fresh herbs.

PER SERVING GLYCAEMIC LOAD 0; PROTEIN 29 G; CARBOHYDRATES 17 G; FAT 17 G (OF WHICH SATURATES 6 G); FIBRE 4 G

 MAKE AHEAD The meat filling can be made 2 days ahead and stored in the refrigerator. It could also be frozen for 2 months. This stuffing can also be used as a sauce for pasta.

Ragout of venison with mushrooms and lentils

2 tablespoons clarified butter

1 onion, finely chopped

100 g (3½ oz) button mushrooms

100 g (3½ oz) chanterelle mushrooms

500 g (1 lb 2 oz) venison, cut into 4 cm (1½ in) cubes

400 g (14 oz) can chopped tomatoes

500 ml (18 fl oz) water, or venison or beef stock

1 teaspoon dried thyme

2 teaspoons fructose

½ teaspoon cinnamon

2 carrots, cut into chunks

1 small leek, sliced

150 g (5½ oz) red lentils, rinsed

3 tablespoons sour cream (optional), plus extra to serve

salt and pepper

1 tablespoon chopped parsley (optional)

1 Melt half the butter in a frying pan, add the onion and cook until soft and golden. Transfer to a saucepan. Melt the remaining butter and cook the mushrooms until just tender. Add to the pan with the onion.

2 Add the venison, tomatoes, water, thyme, half the fructose and the cinnamon. Bring to the boil, then reduce the heat and simmer for 10 minutes. Add the carrots, leek and lentils and cook for a further 15–20 minutes, or until the lentils are soft.

3 Mix in the cream and heat through. Season with salt and pepper and a little more fructose if necessary. Serve hot, sprinkled with parsley and a spoonful of cream if you like. Serve with redcurrants or redcurrant jelly.

PER SERVING GLYCAEMIC LOAD 7; PROTEIN 56 G; CARBOHYDRATES 34 G; FAT 20 G (OF WHICH SATURATES 7 G); FIBRE 5 G

Rabbit casserole with Mavrodaphne

SERVES 4

1½ kg (3 lb 5 oz) rabbit, cut into serving pieces

240 ml (8 fl oz) wine vinegar

2 tablespoons clarified butter

12–14 small onions, peeled

100 ml (3½ fl oz) Mavrodaphne, Madeira or port

3 carrots, sliced

2 bay leaves

½ teaspoon ground cloves

1 piece of cinnamon stick

salt and pepper

100 ml (3½ fl oz) olive oil

2 tablespoons coarsely chopped walnuts

Mavrodaphne is a sweet, fortified Greek wine made from the aromatic mavrodaphne grape. Look for it in wine shops and larger supermarkets, but if it isn't available, you can use Madeira or port as an alternative.

1 Place the rabbit meat in a large bowl. Mix the wine vinegar with 240 ml (8 fl oz) water and pour over the rabbit. Leave to marinate for 2 hours.

2 Melt 1 tablespoon butter in a wide, heavy-based saucepan over a medium heat. Add the onions and cook until soft and golden; remove from the pan and set aside.

3 Remove the rabbit from the marinade and pat dry with kitchen paper. Melt the rest of the butter in the saucepan, add the rabbit and brown lightly all over.

4 Return the onions to the saucepan and pour in the wine. Add the carrots, bay leaves, cloves, cinnamon and pepper, then add the olive oil and 100 ml (3½ fl oz) water. Cover the pan and cook over a medium heat for about 50 minutes, until the meat is tender and falling off the bone.

5 Season the casserole to taste with salt and serve hot, sprinkled with the chopped walnuts.

PER SERVING GLYCAEMIC LOAD 0; PROTEIN 35 G; CARBOHYDRATES 11 G; FAT 42 G (OF WHICH SATURATES 11 G); FIBRE 2 G

Roasted mixed vegetables

SERVES 6

250 g (9 oz) sweet potatoes

250 g (9 oz) celeriac

250 g (9 oz) courgettes (zucchini)

250 g (9 oz) aubergine (eggplant)

1 green and 1 red
pepper (capsicum)

2–3 carrots

2–3 onions

1 large leek

500 g (about 1 lb) tomatoes

4 garlic cloves

4 tablespoons fresh or
dried oregano

2 tablespoons rosemary sprigs

small bunch of fresh mint
(or 2 teaspoons dried mint),
plus extra, to serve

small bunch of fresh parsley, plus
extra, to serve

100 ml (3½ fl oz) olive oil

salt and pepper

*In Greece, this traditional dish is known as briam. Serve it on its
own or as an accompaniment to chicken or roast meat. Don't worry
if you don't have all the vegetables, just increase the quantities of
the ones you have to hand or substitute others: okra and peas are
often used in Greece. Preparing the vegetables for this recipe
takes a little time but the end result is worth the effort.*

1 Preheat the oven to 180°C/350°F/gas 4.

2 Cut the following vegetables into chunks: the sweet potatoes, celeriac,
courgettes, aubergine, peppers and carrrots. Cut the onion into wedges
and the leek into thick rings. Skin and roughly chop the tomatoes and
chop the garlic. Finely chop all the fresh herbs.

3 Place all ingredients in a large bowl and mix well. Tip into a roasting
tin, cover with foil and roast for 40 minutes.

4 Remove the foil and return the pan to the oven for a further
15 minutes. The vegetables are done when they begin to colour.
Remove from the oven and serve warm.

PER SERVING GLYCAEMIC LOAD 10; PROTEIN 4 G; CARBOHYDRATES 25 G; FAT 16 G
(OF WHICH SATURATES 2.5 G); FIBRE 7 G

Vegetarian moussaka

SERVES 12

8 large aubergines
(eggplants), sliced

10 courgettes (zucchini), sliced

10 peppers (capsicums) – red,
orange, yellow and green,
cut into rings

6 tablespoons olive oil

3 onions, finely chopped

salt and pepper

fructose, to taste

8–10 tomatoes, skinned and
roughly chopped

3 tablespoons grated Parmesan

15 slices Edam or
other mild cheese

*In Greece, this would be topped with a mild cows' milk cheese
called Kaseri; Edam is a good substitute.*

1 Preheat the oven to 220°C/425°F/gas 7.

2 Put the aubergines, courgettes and peppers in a roasting tin, drizzle
over 3 tablespoons of the oil and roast in the oven until tender, about
40 minutes.

3 Meanwhile, heat the remaining oil in a saucepan, add the onions,
salt, pepper and fructose and cook over medium heat until the onions
begin to soften. Add the tomatoes and a few tablespoons of water and
simmer until you have a thick sauce, about 15 minutes.

4 Place a layer of roasted aubergines in a lightly oiled, large ovenproof
dish. Season and add some of the tomato sauce, then the Parmesan.
Add a layer of courgettes, then peppers, then sauce, then aubergines,
and so on, seasoning as you go and finishing with a layer of sauce.
Lay the cheese slices on top.

5 Put the moussaka in the oven for 15 minutes, then serve hot.

PER SERVING GLYCAEMIC LOAD 2; PROTEIN 11 G; CARBOHYDRATES 16 G; FAT 13 G
(OF WHICH SATURATES 5 G); FIBRE 6 G

Garlic spinach

SERVES 4

750 g (1 lb 10 oz) spinach

3 tablespoons olive oil

6 spring onions or
1 leek, finely sliced

2 garlic cloves, finely sliced

4 eggs, beaten

salt and pepper

juice of ½ lemon

*A delicious accompaniment to any main course, this is especially good
with lamb dishes. For a Greek touch, add 2 tablespoons of chopped
fresh dill along with the salt and pepper.*

1 Wash the spinach thoroughly and trim off the stalks if they are tough.
Cut the leaves into ribbons about 1 cm (½ in) wide. Place in a large
saucepan over low heat until the spinach wilts, about 3 minutes, stirring
occasionally. Drain thoroughly, squeezing out the excess water.

2 Heat 2 tablespoons of the olive oil in the pan, add the spring onions
or leek and the garlic and cook for 2–3 minutes, until the onions or leeks
begin to soften.

3 Add the spinach and stir over medium heat for a further 2–3 minutes.
Season with salt and pepper, add the lemon juice and the remaining
olive oil and serve at once.

PER SERVING GLYCAEMIC LOAD 0; PROTEIN 5 G; CARBOHYDRATES 4 G; FAT 10 G
(OF WHICH SATURATES 1 G); FIBRE 4 G

Baked aubergines in tomato sauce

SERVES 8

4 large aubergines (eggplant)

8–10 tablespoons olive oil

6 onions (about 500 g/1 lb), sliced into rings

6 garlic cloves

salt and pepper

6 large ripe tomatoes (about 750 g/1½ lb), skinned and roughly chopped

2 tablespoons tomato purée (paste)

2 teaspoons fructose

1 tablespoon dried mint

large bunch of parsley, finely chopped

4 tablespoons grated Parmesan

100g (3½ oz) Gruyère or Cheddar cheese, grated

These baked aubergines are very popular in Greece, but the recipe is actually from Turkey, where it is known as Imam bayildi, *'the priest fainted' – presumably with delight.*

1 Preheat the oven to 180°C/350°F/gas 4.

2 Wash the aubergines and cut in half lengthways. Heat 2 tablespoons oil in a large frying pan, add the aubergines and cook for 3 minutes on each side. Drain on kitchen paper.

3 Heat the remaining oil in a saucepan and add the onion, garlic, salt and pepper. Cook over a medium-low heat until the onions are golden, about 20 minutes.

4 Add the tomatoes to the saucepan, together with the tomato purée, fructose, mint and parsley. Simmer over a low heat until the mixture thickens.

5 Place the aubergines in a roasting tin, skin side down, and divide the tomato mixture among the aubergines. Mix the two cheeses together and sprinkle over the aubergines. Place in the oven for about 20 minutes. Serve warm.

PER SERVING GLYCAEMIC LOAD 0; PROTEIN 9 G; CARBOHYDRATES 12 G; FAT 20 G (OF WHICH SATURATES 6 G); FIBRE 4 G

Leek, mushroom and tomato gratin

SERVES 4

1 tablespoon olive oil

1 onion, sliced

2 garlic cloves, finely chopped

2 large leeks, thinly sliced

200 g (7 oz) mushrooms, quartered

400 g (14 oz) can chopped tomatoes

2 tablespoons tomato purée (paste)

½ teaspoon dried oregano

½ teaspoon dried thyme

salt and pepper

½ teaspoon fructose

60 g (2 oz) feta cheese

This zero GL dish is just as delicious made with courgettes (zucchini) or fennel instead of leeks.

1 Heat the oil in a frying pan over low heat. Add the onion, garlic and leeks and fry gently for 6–8 minutes until the vegetables soften and begin to turn golden.

2 Add the mushrooms and cook for a further 2–3 minutes. Add the tomatoes with their juice, tomato purée and herbs. Leave to simmer for 4–5 minutes. Season with salt, pepper and fructose.

3 Preheat the grill. Put the vegetable mixture into a shallow ovenproof dish and crumble the cheese on top. Place under the grill until the cheese begins to brown and bubble.

PER SERVING GLYCAEMIC LOAD 0; PROTEIN 6 G; CARBOHYDRATES 9 G; FAT 6 G (OF WHICH SATURATES 2.5 G); FIBRE 2.5 G

◄ Courgette gratin

SERVES 4

2 large courgettes
(zucchini), sliced
100 g (3½ oz) feta cheese,
crumbled
4 eggs, beaten
300 ml (10 fl oz) crème fraîche or
sour cream (20% fat or less)
2 garlic cloves, finely chopped
handful of basil leaves, chopped
salt and pepper

This rich, creamy dish looks striking made with a mixture of green and yellow courgettes.

1 Preheat the oven to 180°C/350°F/gas 4. Blanch the courgettes in plenty of boiling water. Drain, cool under running water and drain well.

2 Arrange the courgettes in a shallow ovenproof dish. Sprinkle the feta over the courgettes.

3 Mix the eggs with the cream, then add the garlic, basil, salt and pepper and mix all together. Pour over the courgettes and bake for 15 minutes. Reduce the heat to 150°C/300°F/gas 2 and cook for a further 20 minutes. The finished dish should not look too brown on top.

PER SERVING GLYCAEMIC LOAD 0; PROTEIN 17 G; CARBOHYDRATES 5 G; FAT 23 G (OF WHICH SATURATES 16 G); FIBRE 0.5 G

Baked courgette and fennel omelette

SERVES 4

4 tablespoons olive oil
1 bulb fennel
500 g (about 1 lb) courgettes
(zucchini), grated
1 large red onion,
finely chopped
6 eggs
salt and pepper

1 Preheat the oven to 180°C/350°F/gas 4. Grease a round ovenproof dish with 1 tablespoon of the oil. Halve the fennel and remove the stalk. Cut each half into thin slices.

2 Heat the remaining oil in a sauté pan and add the courgettes. Stir over medium heat until the liquid released by the courgettes has evaporated. Add the onion and fennel, reduce the heat slightly and cook for 8–10 minutes, until the onion begins to soften. Transfer to a bowl to cool for a few minutes.

3 Beat the eggs together with a little salt and pepper and mix them with the vegetables in the bowl. Pour the mixture into the oiled dish and bake in the oven for about 50 minutes or until the omelette has set and the surface is golden. Remove from the oven and leave to cool for a few minutes. Cut into slices and serve.

PER SERVING GLYCAEMIC LOAD 0; PROTEIN 12 G; CARBOHYDRATES 6 G; FAT 19 G (OF WHICH SATURATES 4 G); FIBRE 2 G

Cauliflower with tomatoes and feta ▶

SERVES 4

2 tablespoons clarified butter
1 large onion, sliced
2 garlic cloves, crushed
8 tomatoes, skinned and
finely chopped
2 teaspoons dried oregano
a pinch of cinnamon
salt and pepper
1 large cauliflower, cut into florets
3 tablespoons olive oil
1 tablespoon fresh lemon juice
75 g (2½ oz) feta
cheese, crumbled

*This is particularly good with lamb or other grilled or roast meat.
Or serve with a bean or lentil dish and a salad for a vegetarian feast.*

1 Preheat the oven to 190°C/375°F/gas 5. Melt the butter in a thick-bottomed frying pan over medium heat, add the onion and garlic and cook for 3–4 minutes.

2 Add the chopped tomatoes, oregano, cinnamon and a little salt and pepper. Stir well, then cover and simmer for approximately 5 minutes.

3 Add the cauliflower florets to the tomato sauce, cover and simmer for 10–15 minutes. Remove from the heat.

4 Put the cauliflower and tomato mixture in an ovenproof dish or roasting tin and drizzle the olive oil and lemon juice over. Top with crumbled feta cheese.

5 Bake for approximately 40 minutes, or until the cauliflower is tender and the cheese has melted. Serve hot.

PER SERVING GLYCAEMIC LOAD 0; PROTEIN 8 G; CARBOHYDRATES 11 G; FAT 21 G (OF WHICH SATURATES 9 G); FIBRE 4 G

Broccoli mustard gratin

SERVES 6

2 heads of broccoli,
split into florets
200 ml (7 fl oz) single cream
200 ml (7 fl oz) semi-skimmed milk
1 tablespoon cornflour
1 tablespoon Dijon mustard
90 g (3 oz) Gruyère or Cheddar
cheese, grated
45g (1½ oz) Parmesan
cheese, grated
salt and pepper

*Serve with a mixed salad, or tomato salad with beans and basil
(page 77) for a complete meal.*

1 Preheat the oven to 220°C/425°F/gas 7.

2 Cook the broccoli in lightly salted boiling water for 2 minutes; it should still be slightly crisp. Drain in a colander, rinse under cold water and drain thoroughly.

3 Put the cream and milk in a saucepan and heat to boiling point. Dissolve the cornflour in a little water and whisk it into the hot mixture. Boil rapidly to thicken. Take the sauce off the heat and add the mustard and half the cheese. Season with salt and pepper and mix well.

4 Place the broccoli in an ovenproof dish. Pour the sauce over the broccoli and sprinkle with the remaining cheese. Bake in the oven for about 10 minutes, until the top is golden.

PER SERVING GLYCAEMIC LOAD 0; PROTEIN 13 G; CARBOHYDRATES 9 G; FAT 15 G (OF WHICH SATURATES 9 G); FIBRE 2.5 G

Baked fennel with peppers and roasted tomatoes

SERVES 4

4 tomatoes, ideally
plum tomatoes
salt and pepper
4 fennel bulbs
100 ml (3½ fl oz) olive oil
2 garlic cloves, thinly sliced
1 red pepper (capsicum),
thinly sliced
1 yellow pepper (capsicum),
thinly sliced
½ teaspoon dried oregano
½ teaspoon dried thyme

Roasting the tomatoes intensifies the flavour and gives them a firmer texture. I recommend that you roast more than the four needed for this recipe: they're good in salads or added to chicken or meat dishes.

1 Preheat the oven to 120°C/250°F/gas ½ or the lowest setting. Wash the tomatoes, remove the stalks and slice them in half. Put the tomato halves, cut side up, on a baking sheet covered with non-stick baking paper. Sprinkle the tomatoes with salt and place in the oven for 3–6 hours, depending on how moist you like them. The longer you leave them the more intense the flavour and the drier they will be – almost like sun-dried tomatoes.

2 Increase the oven temperature to 160°C/325°F/gas 3. Slice the fennel bulbs in half vertically; trim off any brown bits. Slice the fennel halves into wedge-shaped pieces – approximately 6 per half fennel bulb. Put the pieces in a roasting tin and pour over half of the oil; season with salt and pepper. Cook for 45 minutes, turning carefully once or twice.

3 Put the rest of the oil in a saucepan over low heat. Add the garlic and cook for 2 minutes. Add the peppers and herbs, increase the heat and sauté until the peppers are just tender. Add the tomatoes and fennel and stir gently. Leave to simmer for 2–3 minutes. Season to taste with salt and pepper. Serve hot.

PER SERVING GLYCAEMIC LOAD 0; PROTEIN 2 G; CARBOHYDRATES 7 G; FAT 23 G (OF WHICH SATURATES 3 G); FIBRE 4 G

MAKE AHEAD You can prepare the roasted tomatoes in advance. They will keep for a week in the refrigerator. Make double or treble quantities: they're very good in salads.

Chickpea fritters

SERVES 6

300 g (10½ oz) dried chickpeas, soaked overnight

8 tablespoons olive oil

2 large onions, chopped

2 garlic cloves, crushed

1 teaspoon ground cumin

1 teaspoon dried thyme

3 tablespoons chopped flat-leaf parsley

1 egg, beaten

6 tablespoons chickpea flour, plus extra to coat

salt and pepper

Serve with Greek salad (page 82) as a main course, or serve as an accompaniment or first course.

1 Rinse the chickpeas thoroughly. Place in a large saucepan with plenty of water, bring to the boil and boil for 10 minutes, then reduce the heat and simmer steadily for 1 hour or until the chickpeas are very soft, skimming occasionally. Drain, reserving about 100 ml (3½ fl oz) of the cooking liquid.

2 Put the chickpeas in a food processor and blend to a paste, adding some of the cooking liquid to achieve a smooth consistency.

3 Heat 3 tablespoons of the oil in a large non-stick frying pan. Add the onion and cook until golden. Add the garlic and cumin and stir until fragrant. Add the thyme and parsley, mix well and set aside.

4 Tip the chickpea purée into a large bowl, add the egg, chickpea flour and the onion mixture and mix thoroughly. Season with salt and pepper. Rinse your hands in cold water to prevent the mixture from sticking; take walnut-sized balls of the chickpea mixture and shape into flat patties. Coat in a little more chickpea flour. Place on a tray lined with non-stick baking paper and place in the refrigerator for at least 1 hour.

5 Heat the remaining oil in a large non-stick frying pan. Add the chickpea fritters and cook, in batches, for 1–2 minutes on each side, until golden brown. Remove with a slotted spoon and drain on kitchen paper. Keep warm while you cook the remaining fritters, adding more oil if necessary. Serve hot or at room temperature, with salad and lemons.

PER SERVING GLYCAEMIC LOAD 5; PROTEIN 19 G; CARBOHYDRATES 43 G; FAT 20 G (OF WHICH SATURATES 3 G); FIBRE 9 G

 MAKE AHEAD The cooked fritters can be refrigerated for 3–4 days. The uncooked mixture can be frozen for up to 2 months.

Yellow split pea purée

SERVES 6

250 g (9 oz) chana dal or
yellow split peas

3 shallots or 1 onion cut into 4

1 garlic clove, peeled

75 ml (3 fl oz) extra virgin olive oil

1 teaspoon cold-pressed flaxseed
oil (for extra omega-3 – optional)

2 tablespoons fresh lemon juice

salt and ground white pepper

1 large bunch of spring
onions, finely chopped

1 heaped tablespoon fresh thyme
leaves or 1 teaspoon dried

fresh flat-leaf parsley or oregano
or finely sliced red onion, to serve

This is one of my childhood favourites; in Greece it is known as fava. *It is served as an accompaniment to fish, meat or vegetable dishes. The best yellow peas come from the volcanic island of Santorini.*

1 Soak the split peas overnight. Drain and rinse well.

2 Put the peas in a large saucepan (not cast-iron), together with the shallots or onion and the garlic. Add plenty of water and bring to the boil. Reduce the heat and simmer gently for 45–60 minutes, until the peas are very soft, stirring and skimming occasionally.

3 Drain and reserve the cooking liquid. Remove the shallots or onions and transfer the peas to a food processor. Add the olive oil, flaxseed oil and lemon juice and blend until smooth and pale (add a little of the reserved cooking liquid if the purée seems too thick). Season to taste with salt and pepper. Add the spring onions and thyme and stir well.

4 Spoon into a serving bowl and, if you like, drizzle with a little more olive oil and lemon juice and sprinkle with herbs or red onion. Serve hot or cold.

PER SERVING GLYCAEMIC LOAD 3; PROTEIN 10 G; CARBOHYDRATES 25 G; FAT 13 G
(OF WHICH SATURATES 2 G); FIBRE 3 G

 MAKE AHEAD This can be stored in the refrigerator for 4–5 days. It can also be frozen for up to 2 months.

White beans with tomatoes

SERVES 4

300 g (10½ oz) butter beans or
other large white beans,
soaked overnight
100 ml (3½ fl oz) olive oil
2 large onions, chopped
2 carrots, diced
2 sticks of celery, diced
3 garlic cloves, sliced thinly
1 teaspoon dried thyme
1 teaspoon dried oregano
400g (14 oz) can
chopped tomatoes
2 tablespoons tomato
purée (paste)
½ tablespoon fructose
salt and pepper
3 tablespoons chopped
fresh parsley

This is a classic Greek dish known as gigantes plaki. *It can be served
hot, warm or cold.*

1 Rinse the beans under cold water and place in a large saucepan.
Add water to cover and bring to the boil. Cook until the beans are
nearly soft – test them after about 1 hour. Drain in a colander.

2 Preheat the oven to 180°C/350°F/gas 4.

3 Heat the oil in a large saucepan over low heat, add the onions and
fry until light golden. Add the carrots, celery, garlic, thyme and oregano
and stir until fragrant.

4 Add the tomatoes and cook for 10 minutes. Add the tomato purée,
300 ml (10 fl oz) hot water and the beans to the pan and mix well.
Add the fructose, salt and pepper and mix well.

5 Pour the mixture into an ovenproof dish and cook in the oven for
about 30 minutes. Test the beans occasionally and add more water
if they seem dry. Add the parsley and leave in the hot oven for
5 minutes before serving.

PER SERVING GLYCAEMIC LOAD 14; PROTEIN 19 G; CARBOHYDRATES 47 G; FAT 25 G
(OF WHICH SATURATES 4 G); FIBRE 14 G

 MAKE AHEAD This dish can be refrigerated for up to 5 days. It can
also be frozen for 2 months.

Black beans with herbs

SERVES 2

400 g (14 oz) can black beans
2 tablespoons olive oil
2 shallots, finely chopped
1 teaspoon fresh thyme, finely chopped
1 teaspoon fresh oregano, finely chopped
2 tablespoons chopped fresh flat-leaf parsley
salt and pepper

Did you know that black beans contain more antioxidants than any other beans?

1 Drain the beans and rinse under cold running water. Place in a saucepan, add water to cover and heat through over a low heat.

2 Heat 1 tablespoon oil in a frying pan over a medium heat. Add the shallots and fry until translucent, then add the herbs. Drain the beans well and add to the frying pan. Mix well and season with salt and pepper. Drizzle the remaining olive oil over the top.

PER SERVING GLYCAEMIC LOAD 6; PROTEIN 13 G; CARBOHYDRATES 30 G; FAT 16 G (OF WHICH SATURATES 2 G); FIBRE 7 G

Puy lentils with red wine

SERVES 2

200 g (7 oz) Puy lentils, or other green lentils
100 ml (3½ fl oz) red wine
2 shallots, finely chopped
2 tablespoons olive oil
2 tablespoons finely chopped herbs, or herb oil (see page 68)
1 tablespoon balsamic vinegar
salt and pepper
a little fructose

Dark green Puy lentils are one of the tastiest varieties of lentil and are a favourite of top chefs.

1 Put the lentils in a saucepan with the wine and 300 ml (10 fl oz) water, bring to the boil, then reduce the heat and simmer until tender – this will take about 30 minutes. The cooking water should have been absorbed completely; add more water during cooking if necessary.

2 Once the lentils are cooked, add the remaining ingredients and cook gently for 5 minutes. Season with salt, pepper and fructose.

PER SERVING GLYCAEMIC LOAD 12; PROTEIN 24 G; CARBOHYDRATES 50 G; FAT 12 G (OF WHICH SATURATES 2 G); FIBRE 9 G

 MAKE AHEAD This dish is best when fresh but leftovers can be stored in the refrigerator for 3–4 days.

Mung bean and tomato salad ▶

Mung beans are tiny green beans that look very much like green lentils. They have a delicate nutty flavour and are packed with heart-healthy soluble fibre.

SERVES 4

200 g (7 oz) mung beans
75 g (2½ oz) rocket
1 large onion, finely chopped
2 large ripe tomatoes, chopped
4 sun-dried tomatoes, cut into strips
2 tablespoons chopped flat-leaf parsley
2 tablespoons chopped walnuts

DRESSING

100 ml (3½ fl oz) olive oil
1 tablespoon cold-pressed flaxseed oil (optional)
1 tablespoon chopped fresh coriander
1 tablespoon chopped fresh thyme (or dried)
1 tablespoon lemon juice
½ teaspoon fructose
1 teaspoon Dijon mustard
salt and pepper

1 Put the mung beans in a saucepan with about 500 ml (18 fl oz) water or stock. Boil for about 40 minutes or until tender, but don't overcook or they will split. Drain well.

2 Soak the rocket in ice-cold water for 10 minutes then drain well, preferably in a salad spinner, and chop roughly.

3 Place the beans, onion, tomatoes, rocket and parsley in a bowl and mix gently.

4 Place all the dressing ingredients in a small bowl and blend with a hand-held blender. Pour the dressing over the salad and mix gently. Sprinkle the walnuts over the top. Serve warm or cold.

PER SERVING GLYCAEMIC LOAD 9; PROTEIN 13 G; CARBOHYDRATES 33 G; FAT 36 G (OF WHICH SATURATES 5 G); FIBRE 8 G

Lentil and bean salad

This recipe features a trio of pulses and has a Mexican influence.

SERVES 4

150 g (5½ oz) yellow lentils
400 g (14 oz) can red kidney beans
400 g (14 oz) can chickpeas
2 sun-ripened tomatoes, diced
1 tablespoon jalapeño chillies (from a jar), finely chopped
1 onion, finely chopped
1 garlic clove, finely chopped
3 tablespoons chopped fresh coriander
2 tablespoons white wine vinegar
4 tablespoons olive oil
1 teaspoon fructose
salt and pepper

1 Rinse the lentils under cold water until the water running off is clear. Cook the lentils in boiling water for 12–14 minutes until almost soft but still retaining a little bite. Drain and rinse under cold water.

2 Rinse the beans and chickpeas under cold running water. Place in a large bowl with the lentils.

3 Add the other ingredients to the bowl and mix everything well. Season with salt and pepper.

PER SERVING GLYCAEMIC LOAD 14; PROTEIN 22 G; CARBOHYDRATES 56 G; FAT 17 G (OF WHICH SATURATES 2 G); FIBRE 11 G

 MAKE AHEAD This dish can be made a day ahead and stored in the refrigerator.

Quinoa with leek and tomato

250 g (9 oz) quinoa
½ teaspoon salt
1 tablespoon clarified butter
170 g (6 oz) leeks, finely sliced
60 ml (2 fl oz) chicken or
vegetable stock
3 tablespoons olive oil
2 yellow or red tomatoes,
deseeded and diced
3 tablespoons chopped
fresh chives
3 tablespoons chopped fresh basil
1 tablespoon fresh lemon juice
salt and pepper

1 Place the quinoa in a strainer and rinse under cold running water until the water running off is clear.

2 Put the quinoa and salt in a saucepan with 480 ml (16 fl oz) water and bring to the boil. Reduce the heat and simmer until the quinoa is almost tender and most of the water has disappeared. This will take around 20 minutes. Drain off the remaining water and set aside.

3 Melt the butter in a saucepan over a medium heat. Add the leeks and sauté until soft. Add the stock, bring to the boil and cook for about 5 minutes.

4 Add the quinoa and olive oil, mix well, and heat through for about 5 minutes. Finally, add the tomatoes, chives, basil and lemon juice and stir gently for a few minutes, until heated through. Season to taste with salt and pepper.

PER SERVING GLYCAEMIC LOAD 15; PROTEIN 9 G; CARBOHYDRATES 50 G; FAT 14 G (OF WHICH SATURATES 4 G); FIBRE 3 G

Herbed quinoa pilaf

685 g (1½ lb) quinoa
¾ teaspoon salt
3 tablespoons olive oil
1½ tablespoons fresh lemon juice
200 g (7 oz) pine nuts,
lightly toasted
1 red onion, finely chopped
3 bunches (60 g/2 oz) fresh
basil, chopped
salt and pepper

1 Place the quinoa in a strainer and rinse under cold running water until the water running off is clear.

2 Put the quinoa and salt in a saucepan with 1 litre (1¾ pints) water and bring to the boil. Reduce the heat and simmer until the quinoa is almost tender and most of the water has disappeared. This will take around 20 minutes. Drain off the remaining water and transfer the quinoa to a large bowl.

3 Using a fork, stir in the olive oil and lemon juice and leave to cool to room temperature.

4 Stir in the pine nuts, red onion and basil. Season to taste with salt and pepper.

PER SERVING GLYCAEMIC LOAD 20; PROTEIN 14 G; CARBOHYDRATES 67 G; FAT 22 G (OF WHICH SATURATES 2 G); FIBRE 3 G

Barley risotto with Parmesan

SERVES 4

1.5 litres (2½ pints) chicken stock
6 tablespoons clarified butter
1 onion, finely chopped
2 garlic cloves, finely chopped
400 g (14 oz) pearl barley
100 g (3½ oz) button
mushrooms, sliced
salt and pepper
50 g (1¾ oz) Parmesan, grated
1 tablespoon finely
chopped fresh chives
1 tablespoon chopped
flat-leaf parsley
1 tablespoon chopped fresh basil

1 Bring the stock to the boil and keep warm.

2 Melt 2 tablespoons butter in a large saucepan over a medium heat. Add the onion and garlic; sauté until the onion is soft but not coloured. Add the barley and stir until the grains are lightly coated with butter.

3 Add 120 ml (4 fl oz) stock and leave to simmer, stirring frequently. Add the remaining stock 120 ml (4 fl oz) at a time, making sure the stock has been absorbed before adding more. Stir frequently so that the grains do not stick to the bottom of the pan. Cook until the barley is tender but still retains a little bite; the dish should look creamy. The cooking process takes around 45 minutes.

4 Meanwhile, melt 2 tablespoons butter in a frying pan, add the mushrooms and sauté until tender, about 4 minutes. Season with salt and pepper.

5 Add the mushrooms, Parmesan, herbs and the remaining butter to the cooked barley. Mix well and season with salt and pepper to taste.

PER SERVING GLYCAEMIC LOAD 22; PROTEIN 14 G; CARBOHYDRATES 89 G; FAT 26 G (OF WHICH SATURATES 16 G); FIBRE 1 G

Basmati rice salad with nuts

SERVES 6

375 g (13 oz) brown basmati rice
115 g (4 oz) spring onions,
finely sliced
150 g (5 oz) celery, finely sliced
40 g (1¼ oz) parsley,
finely chopped
115 g (4 oz) chopped walnuts

DRESSING

5 tablespoons olive oil
5 tablespoons fresh lemon juice
3 tablespoons soy sauce
2½ teaspoons ground cumin
salt and pepper

1 Put the rice and 1 litre (1¾ pints) water in a saucepan and bring to the boil. Cover with the lid and reduce the temperature, then simmer until the rice is tender, about 35 minutes. Drain off any excess water through a sieve. Place the rice in a large bowl and stir with a fork to break up any clumps. Leave to cool.

2 Mix the spring onions, celery, parsley and walnuts into the rice.

3 Place all the ingredients for the dressing in a small bowl and mix well. Pour the dressing over the salad and mix everything well. Season with salt and pepper.

PER SERVING GLYCAEMIC LOAD 21; PROTEIN 8 G; CARBOHYDRATES 53 G; FAT 24 G (OF WHICH SATURATES 3 G); FIBRE 3 G

MAKE AHEAD This dish can be made 3 days ahead. It can also be made with leftover rice, though in this case the salad should be eaten immediately.

Peaches with pomegranates and rosemary ▶

SERVES 4

2 peaches
2 nectarines
40 g (1¼ oz) clarified butter
2 tablespoons fructose
juice of 2 oranges
1 sprig fresh rosemary
1 pomegranate
60 g (2 oz) pistachio nuts,
roughly chopped

This is a delightful and super-healthy dessert. Peaches are low GL, while pomegranates and rosemary are antioxidant champions!

1 Wash and dry the peaches and nectarines and cut into slices. Heat the butter in a frying pan over low heat. Add the peaches and nectarines and heat through for 2 minutes. Add the fructose and leave to caramelise for 2–3 minutes.

2 Add the orange juice and rosemary and simmer for 5–6 minutes, until the liquid begins to thicken. Remove the pan from the heat.

3 Meanwhile, cut the pomegranate in half and remove the seeds, discarding the bitter pith.

4 Divide the peaches and juice between 4 plates. Sprinkle the pomegranate seeds and pistachio nuts over the top.

PER SERVING GLYCAEMIC LOAD 7; PROTEIN 4 G; CARBOHYDRATES 23 G; FAT 13 G (OF WHICH SATURATES 6 G); FIBRE 3 G

Passion fruit crème brûlée

SERVES 4

3 passion fruit
300 ml (10 fl oz) milk
200 ml (7 fl oz) double cream
3 tablespoons fructose,
plus 1 tablespoons to serve
¼ teaspoon ground cardamom
2 eggs
3 egg yolks

1 Preheat the oven to 150°C/300°F/gas 2. Halve the passion fruit and remove the contents with a spoon. Press the contents through a sieve, leaving the pips in the sieve.

2 Place the milk, cream, fructose, cardamom and passion fruit juice in a saucepan. Heat the mixture until the fructose has dissolved. You can use a hand-held blender to ensure that the mixture is completely smooth.

3 Whisk the eggs and egg yolks together in a bowl and pour in the hot milk mixture, stirring constantly. Pour the mixture back into the saucepan through a sieve to remove any threads of egg.

4 Pour the mixture into individual ovenproof dishes placed in a roasting tin. Place the roasting tin in the oven and pour in about 1 litre (1¾ pints) of cold water (to make a bain marie). Cook for 30–40 minutes, until the mixture begins to set; this will vary slightly depending on the depth of the dishes. Remove from the oven and leave to cool.

5 Just before serving, sprinkle fructose over the surface and place under a hot grill or use a blowtorch or brulée iron to caramelise the surface.

PER SERVING GLYCAEMIC LOAD 4; PROTEIN 9 G; CARBOHYDRATES 17 G; FAT 33 G (OF WHICH SATURATES 18 G); FIBRE 0 G

◄Blueberry soup with avocado cream

SERVES 4

500 g (1 lb 2 oz) blueberries
4–6 tablespoons fructose
2 tablespoons cornflour

AVOCADO CREAM

1 avocado
1 egg
150 g (5 oz) unsweetened
fromage frais or quark (1% fat)
2 tablespoons fructose
1 tablespoon lemon
juice (or more, to taste)
¼ teaspoon ground cinnamon

It may sound like a strange combination, but you simply have to try this dessert – it's one of my favourites.

1 Put the blueberries and fructose in a saucepan with 500 ml (18 fl oz) water and bring to the boil. Reduce the heat and simmer for 3–4 minutes. Dissolve the cornflour in 3 tablespoons of cold water and add to the soup, stirring constantly. Leave the soup to cool completely.

2 Put all the ingredients for the avocado cream in a measuring jug or large bowl; blend with a hand-held blender until completely smooth.

3 Pour the blueberry soup into small bowls or soup plates and place a generous spoonful of avocado cream in each.

PER SERVING GLYCAEMIC LOAD 9; PROTEIN 6 G; CARBOHYDRATES 48 G; FAT 7 G (OF WHICH SATURATES 1 G); FIBRE 5 G

Barley pudding with raspberry sauce

SERVES 4

115 g (4 oz) pearl barley
1 litre (1¾ pints)
semi-skimmed milk
½ cinnamon stick
½ teaspoon salt
2 tablespoons fructose
200 ml (7 fl oz) double cream
75 g (2½ oz) unsweetened
fromage frais (1% fat)

RASPBERRY SAUCE

500 g (1 lb 2 oz) raspberries,
fresh or frozen (thawed)
4 tablespoons fructose

This is made like a creamy rice pudding, but is better for your blood sugar level because barley has a lower GI than rice.

1 Place the barley in a heavy-based saucepan with 240 ml (8 fl oz) water and bring to the boil over a medium heat, stirring occasionally.

2 When the water has been absorbed, add the milk, salt and cinnamon and lower the heat. Simmer for about 25 minutes, stirring occasionally and adjusting the heat so that the barley does not burn on the bottom of the pan. Cook to a porridge-like consistency; the barley should be tender. If necessary, add more milk and cook for a bit longer. Transfer the barley pudding to a bowl, sprinkle with 2 teaspoons of the fructose and leave to cool. Place in the refrigerator until completely cold.

3 Whisk the cream and the remaining fructose until thick, then stir in the fromage frais and the barley pudding.

4 For the sauce, blend the raspberries with the fructose, then pass through a sieve. The purée can be served uncooked or brought to the boil and thickened with a little cornflour; I prefer the uncooked version.

5 Serve the barley pudding in bowls with the raspberry sauce poured on top or served separately.

PER SERVING GLYCAEMIC LOAD 16; PROTEIN 16 G; CARBOHYDRATES 80 G; FAT 30 G (OF WHICH SATURATES 18 G); FIBRE 3 G

Cinnamon parfaits with marinated berries

SERVES 6

300 ml (10 fl oz) double cream

2 eggs

3 egg yolks

100 g (3½ oz) fructose

½ teaspoon ground cinnamon

200 g (7 oz) light cream cheese

MARINATED BERRIES

1 vanilla pod

1 piece cinnamon stick

4 tablespoons fructose

500 g (1 lb 2 oz) berries, fresh or frozen

You do not need an ice cream machine to make this simple ice cream. Serve with marinated or fresh berries, or raspberry sauce (page 149).

1 Whisk the cream until stiff and place in the refrigerator. Whisk the eggs and egg yolks with the fructose until thick and pale yellow (this is best done in an electric mixer) then mix in the cinnamon. Stir the cream cheese to soften it, then mix into the whipped cream, carefully folding the cream into the egg mixture.

2 Pour the mixture into 6 individual moulds lined with cling film. Cover with more cling film and place in the freezer. The ice cream will be ready to serve in 6 hours. Remove from the freezer 10–15 minutes before serving.

3 For the marinated berries, place the vanilla, cinnamon and fructose in a saucepan with 200 ml (7 fl oz) water and bring to the boil. Reduce the heat and simmer gently for 10 minutes. Pour the warm marinade over frozen berries, or leave to cool to room temperature if the berries are fresh or thawed. Leave the berries to marinate for at least 1 hour to allow the flavours to develop.

PER SERVING GLYCAEMIC LOAD 7; PROTEIN 8 G; CARBOHYDRATES 35 G; FAT 30 G (OF WHICH SATURATES 18 G); FIBRE 2 G

Raspberry yogurt sorbet

SERVES 4

500 g (1 lb 2 oz) frozen raspberries

90 g (3 oz) fructose, or more, to taste

250 g (9 oz) natural yogurt

1 tablespoon fresh lemon juice

A simple dessert that takes just a few minutes to prepare. It can be made with any frozen berries; strawberries are also delicious.

1 Reserve a few berries for decoration. Place all the ingredients in a food processor and process to the desired consistency. The longer you process it, the thinner the sorbet will be. If you prefer a sweeter sorbet, add more fructose.

2 Serve at once, in glass dishes. Decorate the top with frozen berries.

PER SERVING GLYCAEMIC LOAD 7; PROTEIN 5 G; CARBOHYDRATES 34 G; FAT 1 G (OF WHICH SATURATES 0 G); FIBRE 3 G

Real vanilla ice cream

SERVES 6

200 ml (7 fl oz) whole milk
300 ml (10 fl oz) single cream
2 vanilla pods
5 egg yolks
70 g (2½ oz) fructose
pinch of salt

If you have an ice cream machine and an electric mixer, this luxurious ice cream is not difficult to make. For almond ice cream, use only one vanilla pod and add 40g (1¼ oz) lightly toasted chopped almonds to the chilled mixture before you freeze it.

1 Heat the milk and cream in a saucepan to boiling point, then remove the pan from the heat.

2 Split the vanilla pods and scrape out the contents with a small knife or a teaspoon. Add both the seeds and the pods to the creamy milk and place the pan over the lowest possible heat for about 20 minutes.

3 Whisk the egg yolks and fructose – ideally in a mixer – until light and airy. Remove the vanilla pods from the milk and whisk the milk gradually into the whisked egg yolks. Pour the mixture back into the saucepan. Add a small pinch of salt.

4 Return the pan to the heat and heat the mixture, stirring constantly, until it has thickened enough to coat the back of a spoon; do not let it boil or it will curdle.

5 Strain the mixture into a bowl and leave to cool. When cold, place in the refrigerator until thoroughly chilled. Freeze in an ice-cream maker. Transfer to an airtight container and store in the freezer.

If you do not have an ice cream maker, place the chilled mixture in a metal bowl in the freezer for 30–40 minutes. Take the mixture out of the freezer and whisk – ideally with a hand-held electric whisk – until all the ice crystals have been crushed. Return the mixture to the freezer. Repeat two or three times and then leave the ice cream to solidify.

PER SERVING GLYCAEMIC LOAD 3; PROTEIN 5 G; CARBOHYDRATES 16 G; FAT 15 G (OF WHICH SATURATES 8 G); FIBRE 0 G

'Panna cotta'

SERVES 4

3 leaves of gelatine, soaked
in cold water until soft
300 ml (10 fl oz) semi-
skimmed milk
1 tablespoon honey
2 tablespoons fructose
¼ teaspoon ground cinnamon
150 g (5½ oz) unsweetened
fromage frais (1% fat)
1 orange, peeled and diced
40 g (1¼ oz) walnuts, chopped

This Italian dessert is traditionally made with cream, but to cut down on the fat I've substituted fromage frais. Instead of the orange and walnuts, you could serve this with fresh peaches, strawberries or raspberries.

1 Place the milk, honey, fructose and cinnamon in a saucepan. Bring slowly to the boil and simmer for about 5 minutes over a low heat, then remove the pan from the heat.

2 Squeeze the water out of the gelatine leaves, add them to the milk and stir until the gelatine has completely dissolved. Leave the mixture to cool to about 40°C (test with your finger).

3 Add the fromage frais and beat well, using a hand-held blender if you like. Pour the mixture into 4 glasses and leave to set in the refrigerator for at least 3–4 hours.

4 Mix the diced orange with the walnuts, sweeten to taste with a little fructose and arrange on top of the panna cotta before serving.

PER SERVING GLYCAEMIC LOAD 4; PROTEIN 7 G; CARBOHYDRATES 21 G; FAT 8 G
(OF WHICH SATURATES 1.5 G); FIBRE 1 G

Pears poached in red wine with cardamom sauce ▶

SERVES 4

4 pears
1 bottle red wine
40 g (1¼ oz) fructose
½ teaspoon ground cinnamon (or
1 cinnamon stick, broken)
2–3 cardamom pods
50 g (1¾ oz) shelled
walnuts, chopped

CARDAMOM SAUCE

150 g (5 oz) quark (1% fat) or
natural Greek yogurt (0% fat)
50 g (1¾ oz) fructose
½ tablespoon ground cardamom
juice of ½ lemon

1 Mix all the ingredients for the sauce. Cover and chill to allow the flavours to develop while you cook the pears.

2 Peel the pears, leaving the stalks on. In a deep saucepan, just large enough to hold the pears, bring the wine to the boil with the fructose, cinnamon and cardamom. Reduce the heat and simmer for 5 minutes.

3 Add the pears and simmer for 20–40 minutes, until the pears are just tender when tested with a skewer. Leave to cool in the wine. Lift the pears out of the wine with a slotted spoon and place on a serving dish. Strain the wine into a clean pan and boil until it thickens slightly. Leave to cool then pour over the pears.

4 To serve, sprinkle the pears with a few walnuts; serve the cardamom sauce separately.

PER SERVING GLYCAEMIC LOAD 8; PROTEIN 5 G; CARBOHYDRATES 34 G; FAT 9 G
(OF WHICH SATURATES 1 G); FIBRE 3 G

Baked apples with vanilla sauce

SERVES 4

4 apples

50 g (1¾ oz) shelled
walnuts, chopped

50 g (1¾ oz) fructose

½ teaspoon cinnamon

1 tablespoon butter,
cut into flakes

50 g (1¾ oz) flaked almonds,
lightly toasted

VANILLA SAUCE

½ vanilla pod

90 g (3 oz) fromage frais, quark
or Greek (strained) yogurt

50 g (1¾ oz) fructose

juice of ½ lemon or lime

This recipe works just as well with pears. Instead of the vanilla, you could flavour the sauce with ground cinnamon or cardamom.

1 Preheat the oven to 180°C/350°F/gas 4.

2 Make the vanilla sauce: split the vanilla pod and scrape out the contents with a small knife or teaspoon. Mix with the fromage frais or yogurt and stir in the fructose and lemon or lime juice. Leave in the refrigerator for the flavours to develop.

3 Peel and core the apples and slice into wedges. Place in an ovenproof dish. Sprinkle over the walnuts, fructose and cinnamon and mix well. Dot the surface with butter, then bake for 20 minutes.

4 Sprinkle the almonds over the apples before serving, with the vanilla sauce on the side.

PER SERVING GLYCAEMIC LOAD 10; PROTEIN 7 G; CARBOHYDRATES 40 G; FAT 20 G (OF WHICH SATURATES 4 G); FIBRE 3 G

Pear, apple and apricot compote

SERVES 6

300 g (10½ oz) dried apricots

2 pears

2 apples

grated zest and juice of ½ lemon

50 g (1¾ oz) fructose

1 cinnamon stick

2 cloves

1 teaspoon cornflour

Don't worry if you don't have all three fruits – just use extra of the fruits you do have.

1 Soak the apricots overnight.

2 Peel and core the pears and apples. Cut each fruit into 8 wedges. Drain the apricots. Put all the fruit into a saucepan together with the lemon zest and juice, fructose, cinnamon, cloves and 500 ml (18 fl oz) water. Bring to the boil, then reduce the heat and simmer until the fruit is just tender.

3 Using a slotted spoon, transfer the fruit to a bowl, cover and leave to cool. Simmer the fruit juice for a further 10 minutes. Mix the cornflour with a tablespoon of water and stir into the juice. Bring to the boil, then strain the juice into a jug and leave to cool.

4 When the juice is cold, pour it over the fruit. Serve cold, with yogurt or vanilla sauce (see above).

PER SERVING GLYCAEMIC LOAD 9; PROTEIN 2 G; CARBOHYDRATES 36 G; FAT 0 G (OF WHICH SATURATES 0 G); FIBRE 4.5 G

Wera's fantastic chocolate cake

SERVES 12

a little melted butter
400 g (14 oz) ground almonds
50 g (1¾ oz) plain chocolate
5 eggs
100 g (3½ oz) fructose
2 tablespoons cocoa
2 teaspoons baking powder

FILLING

100 g (3½ oz) butter, at
room temperature
100 g (3½ oz) fructose
1 teaspoon vanilla sugar
2 egg yolks

TOPPING

50 g (1¾ oz) dark chocolate
1 teaspoon vanilla sugar
20 g (¾ oz) unsalted butter
1 teaspoon instant coffee powder
1 tablespoon water

Note that the filling contains uncooked egg yolks.

1 Preheat the oven to 160°C/325°F/gas 3. Grease a 23-cm (9-in) round, deep cake tin with melted butter.

2 Place the almonds and chocolate in a food processor and process until very fine.

3 Using an electric whisk or mixer, whisk the eggs and fructose until very thick and pale. Sift in the cocoa and baking powder and gently mix in the almonds and chocolate. Pour the mixture into the prepared cake tin and cook on the lowest shelf of the oven for 30 minutes or until a thin skewer inserted into the centre of the cake comes out clean.

4 Use a knife to loosen the edges of the cake from the tin. Turn out onto a wire rack and leave to cool.

5 For the filling, beat the butter with the fructose and vanilla sugar. Beat in the the egg yolks.

6 For the topping, put all the ingredients in a small glass bowl and place over a saucepan of gently simmering water, stirring until all the ingredients are well mixed. Set aside until lukewarm.

7 Slice the cake in half horizontally. Spread the filling on the bottom half. Cover with the other half of the cake and spread the chocolate glaze on top. Leave the cake in the refrigerator for a while to set.

PER SERVING GLYCAEMIC LOAD 8; PROTEIN 11 G; CARBOHYDRATES 26 G; FAT 33 G (OF WHICH SATURATES 10 G); FIBRE 3 G

◄ Carrot cake

A glycaemically revamped classic!

SERVES 12

3 large eggs

150 g (5½ oz) fructose

125 ml (4 fl oz) rapeseed (canola) oil

90 g (3 oz) wholewheat spelt flour

45 g (1¾ oz) soya flour

30 g (1 oz) ground almonds

2 teaspoons baking powder

½ teaspoon ground cinnamon

½ teaspoon ground ginger

¼ teaspoon salt

400 g (14 oz) carrots, finely grated

60 g (2 oz) chopped walnuts

ICING

200 g (7 oz) light cream cheese

2 tablespoons fructose

1 tablespoon lemon juice

½ teaspoon vanilla flavoured sugar

1 Preheat the oven to 180°C/350°F/gas 4. Lightly oil a 23 cm (9 in) diameter cake tin.

2 Using an electric whisk or mixer, whisk the eggs and fructose until very thick and pale. Set the mixer to low speed and gently pour in the oil. Add the spelt flour, soya flour, ground almonds, baking powder, cinnamon, ginger and salt. Mix everything well together. Stir in the carrots and walnuts.

3 Put the mixture into the prepared tin. Bake the cake for 40–50 minutes, or until a thin skewer inserted into the centre of the cake comes out clean. Leave the cake to cool in the tin on a wire rack for 15 minutes. Turn the cake out of the tin and leave to cool.

4 Stir together the ingredients for the icing and coat the top and sides of the cake. Leave in the refrigerator for at least 1 hour before serving.

PER SERVING GLYCAEMIC LOAD 9; PROTEIN 6 G; CARBOHYDRATES 28 G; FAT 18 G (OF WHICH SATURATES 2 G); FIBRE 1.5 G

Almond tartlets with cardamom cream and strawberries

SERVES 8

170 g (6 oz) almonds

2 tablespoons fructose

3 tablespoons butter, at room temperature

50 g (1¾ oz) coarse rolled oats

FILLING AND TOPPING

75 g (2½ oz) fromage frais (1% fat)

1 tablespoon fructose

½ teaspoon vanilla sugar

¼ teaspoon ground cardamom

250 g (9 oz) fresh strawberries

1 Preheat the oven to 180°C/350°F/gas 4. Grease 8 individual tartlet tins by brushing them with melted butter.

2 Grind the almonds – but not too finely – with the fructose. Stir in the butter and oats to make a pastry. Divide the pastry into 8 pieces and use to line the tartlet tins. Cook for 10–12 minutes or until the pastry is firm and pale golden. The tartlet cases will be very brittle and must be handled carefully.

3 For the filling, mix the fromage frais, fructose, vanilla sugar and cardamom and spoon into the tartlets. Halve the strawberries and arrange on the cardamom cream.

PER SERVING GLYCAEMIC LOAD 5; PROTEIN 6 G; CARBOHYDRATES 14 G; FAT 17 G (OF WHICH SATURATES 4 G); FIBRE 2.5 G

GL list

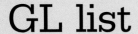

These tables are compiled from information supplied by laboratories in various countries. There are many variables in testing methods, calculation data and composition of food, and sometimes the result is the mean of several studies. Rice, for example, shows a large range of GL values; this variation is due to botanical differences in rice from country to country.

   The first column in the table gives the Glycaemic Index. The second tells you the amount of food containing 50 grams of carbohydrate: this is the amount of food used in laboratory tests to determine the GI. The third column is what I use to calculate the Glycaemic Load (GL) of 100 grams of food, which you will find in the fourth column.

   When looking at the tables think of carbohydrates in terms of high, medium or low GL – rather than being concerned with the specific numbers. I consider a GL of 20 or more as high, 11 to 19 as medium and 10 and below as low.

Foods	GI	Amount of food in grams containing 50 g carbohydrate	Carbohydrate per 100 g of food	GL per 100 g of food
All-Bran (Kellogg's)	42	100	50	21
Apples	38	400	13	5
Apples, dried	29	88	57	16
Apple juice, unsweetened	40	431	12	5
Apricots	57	667	8	4
Apricots, dried	31	107	47	14
Apricots, canned, in light syrup	64	316	16	10
Bagel	72	100	50	36
Baguette	95	100	50	48
Banana	52	250	20	10
Barley, pearl	25	179	28	7
Barley porridge/wholemeal barley flour	68	179	28	19
Beans, baked	48	500	10	5
Beans, black, dried, boiled	20	300	17	3
Beans, black-eyed, dried, boiled	42	250	20	8
Beans, borlotti (brown), dried, boiled	24	100	50	12
Beans, broad (fava), boiled	79	364	14	11
Beans, green, boiled	29	1667	8	2
Beans, haricot (navy), dried, boiled	38	242	21	8
Beans, kidney, dried, boiled	28	300	17	5
Beans, kidney, canned	52	441	11	6
Beans, butter (lima) beans, dried, boiled	32	250	20	6
Beans, butter (lima), canned	36	335	15	5
Beans, mung, dried, boiled	31	441	11	4
Beans, mung, sprouts	25	441	11	3
Beans, pinto, dried, boiled	39	288	17	7
Beans, soya, dried, boiled	18	1250	4	1
Beans, soya, canned	14	1250	4	1
Beetroot	64	571	9	6
Bran flakes cereal	74	83	60	44
Bread, flat Middle Eastern	97	94	53	52
Bread, gluten free, white	76	100	50	38
Bread, hamburger bun	61	100	50	31
Bread, multigrain	43	108	46	20
Bread, oatbran	47	83	60	28
Bread, pitta	57	88	57	32
Bread, pumpernickel	50	125	40	20
Bread, rice	66	116	43	28
Bread, rye, dark (100% wholemeal)	58	107	47	27

Foods	GI	Amount of food in grams containing 50 g carbohydrate	Carbohydrate per 100 g of food	GL per 100 g of food
Bread, sourdough, white flour	54	107	47	25
Bread, soya and linseed	36	166	30	11
Bread, spelt, dark	63	79	63	40
Bread, sunflower and barley	57	151	37	21
Bread, stoneground wholewheat	49	94	53	26
Bread, white	70	98	51	36
Bread, white flour, 80% whole grain	52	75	67	35
Breadfruit	68	222	23	15
Buckwheat	54	250	20	11
Bulgur wheat	48	288	17	8
Carrot, boiled	58	667	8	4
Carrot, raw	16	500	10	2
Carrot juice	43	543	9	4
Cashew nuts	22	192	26	6
Cassava	46	185	27	12
Cheerios cereal	74	75	67	49
Cherries	22	500	10	2
Chickpeas, dried, boiled	28	250	20	6
Chickpeas, chana dal	11	208	24	3
Chickpeas, canned	42	341	15	6
Chocolate, dark, 70% cocoa solids	22	156	32	7
Chocolate, M & Ms, peanut	33	88	57	19
Chocolate, Mars	65	75	67	43
Chocolate, milk	43	89	56	24
Chocolate, Snickers	55	88	57	31
Chocolate, Twix	44	77	65	29
Coca Cola	58	481	10	6
Coco Pops (Kellogg's)	77	58	87	67
Corn, chips	63	96	52	33
Cornflakes cereal	81	58	87	70
Couscous, boiled	58	431	12	7
Cranberry juice	56	431	12	6
Crispbread	64	78	64	41
Croissant	67	110	46	31
Dates, dried	103	75	67	69
Digestive biscuits	55	73	68	37
Doughnut	76	102	49	37
Fanta, orange	68	368	14	9
Frosties (Kellogg's)	55	58	87	48

Foods	GI	Amount of food in grams containing 50 g carbohydrate	Carbohydrate per 100 g of food	GL per 100 g of food
Fructose	19	50	100	19
Grapefruit	25	545	9	2
Grapefruit juice, unsweetened	48	625	8	4
Grapenuts cereal	71	71	70	50
Grapes	46	333	15	7
Glucose	100	50	100	100
Honey	55	69	72	40
Hummus	6	300	17	1
Ice cream, premium (15% fat)	37	278	18	7
Ice cream, low fat (1.2% – 7.1% fat)	43	227	22	9
Just Right cereal	60	64	78	47
Kiwi fruit	53	500	10	5
Lactose	46	50	100	46
Lentils, green, dried, boiled	30	441	11	3
Lentils, green, canned	52	454	11	6
Lentils, red, dried, boiled	26	417	12	3
Lucozade	95	312	16	15
Maltose	105	50	100	105
Mango	51	353	14	7
Marmalade, orange	48	75	67	32
Melon, orange-fleshed	65	1000	5	5
Milk, buttermilk	11	1136	4	0
Milk, full-fat	27	1042	5	1
Milk, semi-skimmed	29	1000	5	1
Milk, skimmed	32	962	5	2
Milk, soya	42	714	7	3
Millet, boiled	71	208	24	17
Muffin	57	102	49	28
Muesli (Alpen)	55	79	63	35
Muesli, unsweetened	49	76	66	32
Noodles, instant	47	225	22	10
Noodles, mung bean/transparent	33	200	25	8
Noodles, rice	61	231	22	13
Noodles, Chinese vermicelli	58	231	22	13
Oatcakes	57	79	63	36
Oranges	42	545	9	4
Orange juice, unsweetened	46	481	10	5
Papaya	59	353	14	8
Parsnip, boiled	97	333	15	15

Foods	GI	Amount of food in grams containing 50 g carbohydrate	Carbohydrate per 100 g of food	GL per 100 g of food
Pasta, brown rice, boiled	92	237	21	19
Pasta, corn, boiled	54	214	23	13
Pasta, fettucine (durum wheat), boiled	40	196	26	10
Pasta, gnocchi (potato-based)	68	188	27	18
Pasta, macaroni, boiled	47	188	27	13
Pasta, spaghetti, al dente	39	191	26	10
Pasta, spaghetti, boiled 10–15 mins	43	188	27	11
Pasta, spaghetti, protein-rich/low-carb, boiled	27	173	29	8
Pasta, spaghetti, wholewheat, boiled	37	214	23	9
Peaches	42	545	9	4
Peaches, canned, in juice	38	545	9	3
Peanuts	14	417	12	2
Pears	38	545	9	3
Pears, canned, in juice	43	545	9	4
Peas, green, fresh	48	571	9	4
Pineapple	59	462	11	6
Pineapple juice, unsweetened	46	357	14	6
Pizza (approx. 5 toppings, GI varies from 30 to 80)	60	185	27	16
Plums	39	500	10	4
Polenta, boiled	68	577	9	6
Popcorn	72	91	55	40
Porridge, made from oatbran	55	500	10	5
Porridge, made from rolled oats	58	568	9	5
Porridge, instant	66	481	10	7
Potato, boiled, peeled	88	417	12	11
Potato, boiled, unpeeled	80	441	11	10
Potato, crisps (chips)	54	102	42	23
Potato, chips/French fries	75	259	19	15
Potato, instant, mashed	85	375	13	11
Potato, jacket	85	250	20	17
Potato, mashed	74	375	13	10
Potato, new, boiled in skin	57	357	14	8
Potato, new, canned	63	417	12	8
Potatoes, steamed	65	278	18	18
Prunes, pitted, ready-to-eat	29	91	55	16
Puffed wheat cereal	74	71	70	52
Pumpkin, boiled	75	1000	5	4
Quinoa	35	294	17	6

Foods	GI	Amount of food in grams containing 50 g carbohydrate	Carbohydrate per 100 g of food	GL per 100 g of food
Raisins	64	68	73	47
Ravioli, with meat	39	237	21	8
Rice, basmati, white	58	197	25	15
Rice, basmati, precooked in pouch	57	185	27	15
Rice, brown	55	227	22	12
Rice, jasmine	109	179	28	31
Rice, parboiled/converted (Uncle Ben's)	47	208	24	11
Rice, risotto/arborio	69	143	35	24
Rice, white, long-grain	56	183	27	15
Rice, white, long-grain, Bangladeshi	38	192	26	10
Rice, wild	57	238	21	12
Rice cakes	91	60	83	76
Rye, whole grain, boiled	34	66	76	26
Scones	92	139	36	33
Shredded Wheat cereal	75	76	66	49
Special K (Kellogg's)	54	71	70	38
Sponge cake	54	95	53	29
Sports drink, Gatorade	78	833	6	5
Sports drink, Isostar	70	694	7	5
Strawberries	40	2000	3	1
Sugar (sucrose)	68	50	100	68
Sultanas	56	66	75	42
Swede	72	750	7	5
Sweet potatoes, cooked	61	268	19	11
Sweetcorn, fresh	53	234	21	11
Taco shells, corn	68	83	60	41
Tomato juice	38	1389	4	1
Tortilla, Mexican	52	104	48	25
Watermelon	72	1000	5	4
Weetabix cereal	70	79	63	44
Wheat, wholegrain, boiled	41	74	68	28
Yakult	46	278	18	8
Yam	66	208	24	16
Yogurt, fat-free, natural, unsweetened	33	625	8	3
Yogurt, fat-free, soya, with fruit and sugar	50	385	13	7
Yogurt, fat-free, with aspartame	14	769	7	1
Yogurt, fat-free, with fruit and sugar	33	323	16	5
Yogurt, low-fat, with fruit and sugar	33	303	16	5
Yogurt, low-fat, with fruit and aspartame	14	862	6	1

Frequently
asked questions

Q How does the Greek Doctor's Diet differ from low-carb diets?

A Most low-carb diets severely restrict the intake of carbohydrates in order to encourage the body to burn fat. My diet, although it contains less carbohydrate than many people are used to, is not low carb but 'slow' carb.

The theory behind diets that severely limit or omit carbohydrates altogether is that when the body does not have a sufficient supply of glucose (which is provided by carbohydrates), it has to burn fat as an energy source. This process, known as ketosis, begins about 24 hours after no carbohydrates have been eaten. Breaking down body fat leads to the formation of substances called ketones, which the body can use as energy instead of blood sugar to a certain extent. Although this sort of approach will result in short-term weight loss, it is not a balanced or healthy long-term diet. Not only does it give you bad breath, but more importantly it causes you to lose fluids and important minerals through increased urination, which you would then need to replace with supplements.

My aim is to provide a balanced, sensible diet, based on both traditional wisdom and cutting-edge scientific knowledge, that you can – and more importantly that you will want to – follow for the rest of your life. It is designed to restore a more natural balance of the types of carbohydrates, proteins and fats you eat. Therefore I do not advocate going through different steps or phases with severe restriction of any food. I want you to improve your health and weight permanently. This means eating more natural foods and fewer refined and processed foods. This is particularly relevant with regard to carbohydrates, because the type of carbohydrate we eat affects our blood sugar levels and these are closely connected with hunger, cravings and the extent to which we store or burn fat. Slow carbs cause a gradual rise in blood sugar levels while processed carbs cause it to spike, which can lead to a myriad of health problems. So, although carbs in general have acquired a tarnished image recently, there is no need to deny yourself them altogether – simply choose wisely. The GL list on pages 159–63 is designed to help you do just that. And don't forget that your choice of healthy, minimally processed fats is extremely important, too.

Q You mention inflammation frequently – isn't this a minor problem, unconnected to diet?

A You may be surprised to learn that inflammation is in fact involved in every type of chronic disease. Inflammation is a natural and necessary reaction: when you get a sprain or burn the affected area becomes red and swollen. This is caused by hormone-like substances called eicosanoids, whose job it is to fight the assault. However, under certain conditions, inflammation can become chronic and exacerbate an existing condition or cause chronic disease.

Chronic inflammation means that something has gone very wrong with your health. Instead of repairing your body – which is the purpose of localized, temporary inflammation – chronic inflammation breaks it down, speeds up the ageing process and causes disease. Inflammatory diseases have increased dramatically in recent decades, in tandem with the increased consumption of omega-6-rich vegetable oils, trans fatty acids and the processed foods containing them. These so-called pro-inflammatory foods are known to encourage inflammation and should be avoided. Increasing your intake of anti-inflammatory foods decreases inflammation and promotes good health. Omega-3 fatty acids (found in fatty fish, flaxseed oil and to a lesser degree in nuts) and antioxidant-rich foods such as vegetables and fruit, berries and herbs, nuts and seeds are anti-inflammatory.

Q Do you advocate the use of supplements?

A First let me point out that having a well-balanced and varied diet is the best thing you can do to achieve good health – supplements are not magic bullets that can make you well if your lifestyle is unhealthy. Too many people put their faith in vitamin and mineral supplements when they need to put more effort into eating properly.

That said, many of us are likely to need special supplements at certain times, for example because of illness or when pregnant or breastfeeding. Vegans need to take vitamin B12, as this vitamin is only found in animal food sources; vegetarians can obtain vitamin B12 from eggs, cheese and milk.

However, it could also be argued that a multivitamin and mineral supplement is an inexpensive health insurance premium for most people. The reasoning behind this is that in the modern world we are all subject to environmental pollutants and stress, which can increase our bodies' needs for additional vitamins and minerals; also, much of the food we eat today no longer has the same nutritional value it once did (due to modern farming methods, soil depletion, long-distance shipping of produce and so on).

If you feel dietary supplements are appropriate for you, I suggest you discuss it with your doctor, as some are contra-indicated if you are taking other medications.

Q How do I overcome my cravings for sweet and starchy foods?

A Ensure you eat regularly and in particular don't miss breakfast or your mid-morning and late-afternoon snacks, as these are important in keeping the blood sugar balanced (they are also the meals that people most often skip). If you miss breakfast it is virtually guaranteed that by mid-morning your body will be craving whatever will raise your blood sugar fastest – and that's sweet, highly refined carbs! The same goes for your snacks. It is also important to include protein in every meal and snack, as protein is more satiating than carbohydrate alone. If you opt for fruit in order to satisfy your need for something sweet, this should also be accompanied by protein – for example some nuts.

Following the Greek Doctor's Diet should reduce your appetite for sweet or starchy foods, as you will not be subject to the same swings in blood sugar that often cause cravings. However, if you continue to suffer from cravings you may want to try the supplement 5-HTP (5-hydroxytryptophan). It has been proven to suppress appetite, especially the craving for sweets and starches. The effect is probably due to the fact that 5-HTP increases the level of serotonin, the brain chemical that has a soothing, calming effect. Several foods, including sugar and chocolate, are known to increase the level of serotonin in the brain. 5-HTP is produced in the body from tryptophan, an amino acid found in most protein foods. A well-balanced diet that includes sufficient protein in all meals will ensure an adequate intake of 5-HTP under normal circumstances.

There have been no reports of serious side effects, though drowsiness may occur if taken during the day, and it is not suitable for pregnant or lactating women. Start by taking 25 to 50 milligrams approximately one hour before bedtime a couple of times a week. Then gradually increase the number of nights you take it, until you take it every night. It is important not to buy a food supplement that contains other ingredients in addition to 5-HTP. Some of these supplements may contain Ephedra (or the Chinese herb Ma Huang, containing Ephedra), which has been linked to serious side effects and should be avoided.

Q The GL of some foods is higher than I expected. Oatcakes are a good example – they appear to have a high GL of 36 when I thought they were medium or low GL. Can you explain?

A I present the GL of foods per 100 grams, not per serving size. This allows for easy comparison between foods and is similar to the way nutritional labels are presented. It is therefore important that you consider the size of the portion you eat. The GL of 100 g of oatcakes may be high, but 100 g of oatcakes is about 10 oatcakes – a lot more than most people would eat in a normal serving. If you were to eat 2 oatcakes, the GL would be 7, which is much more acceptable.

Remember, however, that this principle works in reverse, too. A 100 g serving of cooked pasta may have a medium GL of around 13 but many people eat far larger portions than 100 g; if you eat 200 g the GL will be 26. This is why portion control is such an important part of weight loss. The best way to achieve portion control without having to count grams or calories is to focus on food choices and the composition of your plate, and by eating frequent low-glycaemic meals and snacks. The satiety this provides regulates appetite and leads to automatic control of total food intake.

Q What is fructose and why do you recommend its use?

A Fructose is the form of sugar found in all fruit. It is 30 to 50 per cent sweeter than ordinary sugar (it tastes sweeter in powder form than in liquid form), so you use 30 to 50 per cent less to obtain the same level of sweetness and hence take in fewer calories. Fructose also causes considerably less tooth decay. Most importantly, fructose is absorbed more slowly and cannot be converted into energy immediately, hence it has a low GI of 19.

That does not mean you should use it in unlimited quantities: you should reduce your intake of all types of sugar, but use small amounts of fructose where necessary instead of ordinary sugar. I use it where a little sweetness is required in a savoury recipe or when I'm baking the occasional sweet treat. When adapting your own recipes, you will need about one-third less fructose than sugar. For baking, reduce the oven temperature by around 50°C and bake for slightly longer than you would for recipes containing sugar.

You'll find fructose in powder form in the baking aisle of the supermarket, or in health food shops. It is more expensive than sucrose – which is partly why the food industry has shunned it in favour of

sucrose – but it is worth the extra expense. Pure fructose powder is not the same as high fructose corn syrup or HFCS, which is used in many processed foods and sweetened beverages. HFCS is almost identical to regular sugar (sucrose), but comes in liquid form and is derived from maize. HFCS is high-glycaemic and should be avoided.

Q Why does honey have a high GI if it contains fructose?

A Honey is a water solution of glucose and fructose in varying proportions: it does not have a standard GI because it is not a standard product. The GI of honey varies according to the ratio of glucose to fructose; the more fructose, the lower the GI. I have heard, but cannot verify, that the thinner the honey, the more fructose it contains. If so, this suggests that thin honey might be better than thicker honey.

Q Peanuts have a low GI. Would that be fresh peanuts or salted?

A All peanuts have the same GI, but raw peanuts are a much healthier option than salted or dry roasted, both because of the salt and other additives, and because the peanut fat is heated during roasting/processing.

Q When they are in season, I eat strawberries almost every day. Will this affect my blood sugar levels?

A All berries have a low GI. Strawberries have such a low carbohydrate content that their GI is almost insignificant, so you can eat as many strawberries as you like with a clear conscience. Try raspberries, too – they are particularly rich in fibre and vitamin C. You could add some natural yogurt or cottage cheese to your berries for a better protein balance.

Q How is GI affected by heating? I know that foods such as potatoes have a higher GI when they are cooked but what about other foods, such as rice?

A No general rule applies here. However, foods rich in starch, such as potatoes, carrots, turnips and other root vegetables often get a higher GI when they are cooked because the starch they contain is converted from amylose to amylopectin (of the two types of starch, amylopectin has the higher GI). Vegetables which are not high in starch do not have an increased GI when cooked. The GI of rice increases with cooking time: generally the stickier the rice, the higher the GI. This is why jasmine rice has a higher GI than long-grained basmati.

Q I like to bake – what are the alternatives to white flour?

A Instead of white flour, choose stoneground wholemeal flour. Soya flour, which is very high in protein and has a low GI, can be used to replace about one third to a half of the white flour in most recipes. You can also use oat flour or flour from ancient wheat types such as spelt and kamut; the latter contain more vitamins, minerals and protein than regular wheat flour. Try using them instead of a proportion of white flour. Also remember that the more nuts and seeds you use in a bread, the lower its glycaemic effect and the healthier it becomes.

When baking cakes, you can if you wish replace all the white flour with one-third soya flour, one-third barley flour and one-third finely ground almonds. You may have to adjust the amount of liquid in the recipe to achieve the same result that you do with regular flour. It takes some experimenting, but it's worth the effort.

Q I drink a lot of coffee. Should I avoid caffeine altogether or will cutting back be sufficient? Is tea any better?

A The issue of whether or not coffee is healthy is a contentious one. There has actually been quite a bit of research that has shown favourable results. Coffee drinkers, for example, appear to suffer less asthma, and caffeine is associated with a lower risk of developing Parkinson's disease. Even more importantly, a number of large studies have shown

that those with a moderate intake of coffee have about a 40 per cent lower risk of developing type 2 diabetes. Coffee is, in fact, one of the most significant sources of antioxidants in Western diets, mainly because coffee consumption is so high.

On the negative side, coffee has been found to increase homocysteine levels in the blood, which is associated with a greater risk of Alzheimer's and cardiovascular disorders. However, there is no direct evidence of a connection between coffee drinking and these disorders. Coffee has also been shown to impair fertility among non-smoking women. In addition, it contains acrylamide and cadmium, potentially carcinogenic substances.

There is no doubt that coffee also provides pleasure, so taking the above into account I recommend moderation rather than abstinence or excess. Limit yourself to one or two cups of regular coffee a day or choose decaffeinated coffee instead; if necessary wean yourself off caffeine with a mix of half regular, half decaffeinated coffee.

Black tea also contains caffeine. A far better choice is green tea, which is packed with even more antioxidants than black tea or coffee. Some of the antioxidants have been found to be more powerful than vitamins C and E. Green tea drinkers seem to have a lower risk of a wide range of diseases, from simple infections to chronic degenerative conditions, including cardiovascular disease, cancer and osteoporosis.

Whatever your beverage of choice, bear in mind that the most important source of fluid for the body is water. Aim to drink at least 2 litres (about 8 glasses) of water a day.

Q I often eat out at restaurants. Will the Greek Doctor's Diet fit in with my lifestyle?

A It is becoming much easier to eat healthy food in all sorts of restaurants. The key is to bear in mind the plate models (see page 21) and the general guidelines of the Greek Doctor's Diet. Probably the most practical approach is to make your restaurant meal your ABC meal of that day. This will allow you

to enjoy some carbohydrate such as potatoes, pasta or rice, or a dessert. The following general guidelines will also help:

► Have a small snack before you arrive at the restaurant so that you're not so ravenously hungry that you will eat anything. The snack should be high protein and high fibre (nuts and fruit for example).

► Avoid the bread basket. All bread is medium or high GI and will increase your blood sugar and insulin and even your appetite.

► If possible, opt for a salad dressed with vinaigrette as your starter, as this will lower the GL of the rest of the meal (this is because acidic foods such as vinegar and lemon juice have the effect of slowing down carbohydrate absorption). If you choose a soup, avoid thick creamy ones and opt for those based on stock.

► Avoid anything that is battered or deep-fried. If it isn't obvious how a dish is cooked, then ask.

► Restaurants offer a great opportunity to increase your intake of fish, which most people don't eat enough of. Steamed, grilled, baked or lightly stir-fried fish and seafood is great, but avoid fishcakes and breaded, battered or crumbed dishes.

► If you opt for meat as your source of protein, choose poultry or lean cuts of meat and avoid processed meats such as sausages, pâté and pies.

► Have plenty of vegetables and don't forget pulses, which are a wonderfully healthy way of filling up.

► Be aware of portion sizes, particularly when having the carbohydrate part of your reward meal. Remember it should be half the size of your palm.

► If you are having dessert, choose one based on dairy products, eggs and/or nuts rather than one made with flour.

Index

Recipe index